diabetes
EAT & ENJOY

THE AUTHORS

Christine Roberts is Director of Melbourne Dietetic Centre and Consultant Dietitian to hospitals, commercial organisations and in private practice. She has been involved with diet and diabetes for many years, and has co-authored a number of papers. She was a member of the Working Party for Nutritional Resources, Diabetes Australia, in 1988.

She co-authored the successful *Food for Sport Cookbook* and the *Healthy Heart Cookbook* (for the National Heart Foundation). She was also a contributor to Prof. Pincus Taft's book, *Diabetes Mellitus*.

Jennifer McDonald is Chief Dietitian at Fairfield Hospital and consultant to a number of other organisations. She has been involved in writing many publications for people with diabetes.

She has co-authored a number of scientific papers dealing with diet and diabetes, in association with other top researchers in the field. Her most recent, *'Temporal Study of Metabolic Change when Non-Insulin Diabetes changed from low to high carbohydrate-fibre diet'*, was published in the American Journal of Clinical Nutrition, 1988.

Margaret Cox has been involved in both research and clinical work with people with diabetes for many years. For three years she was nutrition co-ordinator at the Lions International Diabetes Institute, one of Australia's leading diabetes research and educational organisations, and was involved in the development of diabetes education programmes and educational resources for people with diabetes.

She co-authored the *Healthy Heart Cookbook* for the National Heart Foundation.

diabetes
EAT & ENJOY

Christine Roberts • Jennifer McDonald • Margaret Cox

First published in the UK in 1994 by
New Holland (Publishers) Ltd
24 Nutford Place, London W1H 6DQ

10 9 8 7 6 5 4

First published and distributed in Australia by
New Holland Publishers
3/2 Aquatic Drive
Frenchs Forest NSW
Australia

ISBN 1 85368 328 0

Editor: Alison Leach
UK consultant: Ann Hargreaves
Food styling: Ann Creber, Melbourne
Designer: Lynda Patullo, Green Poles Design, Melbourne
Typesetting by Hirt & Carter (Pty) Ltd
Reproduction by Hirt & Carter (Pty) Ltd
Printed and bound in Singapore by Kyodo Printing Co Pte Ltd

Cover photograph: J. B. Fairfax Press Pty Ltd/Ashley Mackevicius

All meal plans in this book have been presented as samples only. Anyone wishing to follow
these meal plans should first seek the advice of a qualified dietician.

AUTHORS' ACKNOWLEDGEMENTS

There are a number of people who have helped and encouraged us in the writing of this book.

We would like, firstly, to acknowledge DIABETES AUSTRALIA, their Health Care and Education Committee, and their National Marketing Committee, for their support.

We'd especially like to thank Jacqui Roberts for undertaking the difficult task of analysing the recipes and meal plans.

The expertise, advice and hard work of René Gordon, our publisher, and her assistants Joy Bowers, Joslin Guest and Des Carroll have made this book a reality. The splendid colour photography is the work of Ann Creber, Lyn Zeeng and Lynda Patullo and we appreciate their skill and creativity.

Most importantly, we thank our families, and especially our husbands Noel Roberts, Michael Hall and Jack Cox — without their support, patience, encouragement and understanding, we could never have completed *EAT & ENJOY*.

Christine Roberts

Jennifer McDonald

Margaret Cox

TABLE OF CONTENTS

WHERE TO GO FOR FURTHER HELP

DIETITIANS

- Ask your GP to refer you to a dietitian at your local hospital and he/she will be able to tailor a diet specifically to your needs.

BRITISH DIABETIC ASSOCIATION

- Youth issues offering contact network, organized activity holidays and family weekends.
- The Diet Information Services helps you to understand and vary your diet offering recipe developments and general advice.
- Advice is given on subjects such as insurance, pregnancy, travel and employment.

There are over 400 branches and groups where members get together for regular meetings, and fund-raising events.

There are various specialist groups including self-help, young people with diabetes, visually impaired and Asian groups.

As a member you will receive *Balance* magazine every two months. This helps to keep you in touch with:

- progress in medical care and research association activities
- menu suggestions
- personalities and people with diabetes in the public eye
- latest legislation affecting people with diabetes
- practical hints on day-to-day problems

Balance is also available on cassette for those with visual problems.

Funding research

Well over £2 million is spent each year to look into new treatments of diabetes, social and medical problems of the condition and to find a cure or means of prevention.

So who has diabetes?

Diabetes affects about 2 per cent of the UK population — 750000 diagnosed (of whom approximately 18000 are under 20 years old) and an estimated 250000 undiagnosed. Over 60000 cases diagnosed each year (3200 under 20 years old).

About 25 per cent of all people with diabetes are treated by insulin injections and diet.

About 75 per cent of all people with diabetes are non-insulin dependent which is common in the elderly and overweight. Thirty per cent of these are treated by diet alone and about 50 per cent are treated by diet and tablets. The remaining 20 per cent need insulin injections to control their blood sugar levels.

INTRODUCTION

Nowadays, people are becoming more health-conscious and manufacturers are responding by producing more low-calorie, reduced-sugar foods. In general, the diet advocated for diabetes is not a special diet, it is a healthy diet recommended for everyone. These recommendations can be summarized as follows:

1   Avoid being overweight. It is more difficult to control your diabetes if you are overweight.

2   Eat regular meals and include a wide variety of foods in your diet.

3   Try to eat more high-fibre, carbohydrate foods, such as wholemeal bread, jacket potatoes, beans and lentils. This will help to control your diabetes.

4   Reduce your intake of sugar and sweet foods, such as desserts, cakes, chocolate and sugary drinks.

5   Reduce your intake of fried and fatty foods, such as full-fat milk, cheese, butter and margarine. These foods are very high in calories.

6   Avoid special diabetic products, such as diabetic sweets, chocolate and biscuits. These are not necessary, may contain the same amount of fat, and, therefore, will not be significantly lower in kilojoules (calories).

7   Use salt in moderation for good general health.

8   Drink alcohol in moderation.

This book is aimed at people with diabetes and people who cook for friends and relatives with diabetes. There are also calorie-counted recipes based on healthy-eating principles for people who wish to lose weight.

Diet Information Services

The British Diabetic Association

KNOWLEDGE IS SWEET

Diabetes mellitus is not new. It may be as old as humanity. Certainly, it has been with us throughout recorded history, but only in 1921 did we learn to treat it with some effectiveness. And only in the past decade have we devised a new way of eating for people with diabetes. In the past 60 or so years, diabetes has changed from being a life-threatening condition to one that requires a change of lifestyle and, where necessary, medication.

WHAT IS DIABETES?

You need to know what diabetes is before you can take an active part in managing your own health care.

'Diabetes' comes from the ancient Greek word for 'siphon', referring to the large amount of sugar-containing urine passed by people with uncontrolled diabetes, and 'mellitus' for the characteristic sweet taste of the urine. **Diabetes (more accurately diabetes mellitus) is simply too much sugar in the blood.**

This sugar is in the form of **glucose.** Diabetes occurs when the system which controls the amount of glucose in the blood no longer works properly.

But where does it all begin? **Everyone** has glucose in their blood all the time. It provides energy (or fuel) to keep the body working, much like the petrol in a motor car.

Where does glucose come from?

Glucose comes from the food we eat. When we eat carbohydrate (sugars and starches), our bodies convert it into glucose.

Some of the foods rich in carbohydrate:

- Breads, cereals and biscuits

- Pulses (such as dried peas, beans and lentils)

- Starchy vegetables (such as potatoes)

- Rice and pasta

- Fruit

- Sugar

- Foods with sugar added, such as cakes, sweet biscuits, confectionery, sweetened soft drinks and canned fruit.

The digestive system breaks down carbohydrate to make glucose. The glucose is then absorbed into the bloodstream directly from the digestive tract or gut.

What happens to the glucose?

The blood carries the glucose to your body tissues (for instance, your brain, lungs, heart, liver, kidneys and muscles). There, the glucose passes from your blood into the tiny cells that make up body tissues. This is where insulin comes into play. The only way in which the glucose in your blood can pass into the cells is with the help of the hormone, insulin. This is because on the walls of each tiny cell are special 'receptor' sites. The insulin attaches itself to the glucose in your blood and locks itself into the receptor sites on the cell walls. There it acts as a sort of conduit, or bridge, allowing the glucose to move through the cell wall into the cell where your body uses it for fuel.

Insulin is produced by the pancreas, a small gland that lies behind the stomach. Scattered throughout the pancreas are clusters of specialized cells, the islets of Langerhans, which make and store insulin, and then release it into the bloodstream as needed. The pancreas, despite its small size, also produces digestive juices which help your body to break down food as it passes through the gut.

After you have eaten, digested and absorbed food containing carbohydrate, the amount of glucose in your blood increases. In response to this, the pancreas releases the correct amount of insulin into your blood to carry the extra glucose into the cells. The amount of glucose in your blood then returns to its pre-meal level. At least, that's the way the system is supposed to work.

If you don't have diabetes, your blood glucose level never goes too high or too low, no matter how much or how little carbohydrate you eat. The system balances itself.

What happens when diabetes develops?

When the body produces little or no insulin or, for various reasons, the insulin it does produce is unable to carry glucose into your body cells, you develop diabetes.

With your normal glucose regulating system out of order, your level of blood glucose keeps on increasing. When it reaches a certain level, the body attempts to tackle the problem by passing the extra glucose out of your body via your urine. This is called 'glycosuria' — literally 'glucose urine'. Not surprisingly, with it comes symptoms such as:

● Passing large amounts of urine by day and night (polyuria meaning 'much urine', and nocturia meaning 'night urine').

● Feeling very thirsty most of the time and having a dry mouth caused by the large urine output.

● Drinking excessively (this goes under the rather melodious scientific name of polydipsia) in response to thirst.

- Losing weight because the normal fuel, glucose, is not available and the body breaks down fat stores.

- Itchiness and infections due to the increased blood and urine glucose.

- Blurring of vision due to the effect of the high blood glucose.

A medical examination will then reveal a high blood glucose level, in other words, a diagnosis of diabetes.

> *A high blood glucose level is known as hyperglycaemia, from 'hyper', meaning excessive, and 'glycaemia' for sugar in the blood.*

What is normal blood glucose level?

A normal blood glucose range for a person without diabetes is between 3.5 and 5.9 mmol/litre.

A fasting blood glucose level greater than 7.8 mmol/litre or a random (that is, not fasting) glucose level greater than 11.1 mmol/litre confirms a diagnosis of diabetes.

NB: Fasting blood glucose is checked when you have been without food or drink for 10 – 12 hours. A random test can be taken at any time, regardless of whether you have eaten or not.

TYPES OF DIABETES

There are two main types of diabetes:

- Insulin-Dependent Diabetes Mellitus (IDDM) — Type 1

- Non-Insulin Dependent Diabetes Mellitus (NIDDM) — Type 2

Insulin-Dependent Diabetes Mellitus (IDDM) — Type 1

IDDM can develop at any age, but usually does so in childhood, during the teens or in early adult-hood. What causes it is unknown, but it may be caused by a virus which leads to the destruction of the islets of Langerhans within the pancreas. Whatever the cause, the pancreas stops making insulin and symptoms appear quickly and severely.

If not treated promptly, your blood glucose level rises. As the glucose cannot get into the cells, your body begins burning up its fat stores too quickly (ketosis) and your breath smells of acetone. You may vomit, become dehydrated and feel drowsy. Left untreated, you will eventually lapse into a coma.

About 25 per cent of all people with diabetes have this type. The treatment is a combination of insulin injections and the healthy diet we present in this book. It is necessary to inject insulin, because if you were to take it by mouth, it would be destroyed by your digestive juices long before it could be absorbed and used.

Non-Insulin Dependent Diabetes Mellitus (NIDDM) — Type 2

This is by far the more common of the two types of diabetes. It develops slowly and symptoms, if any, are likely to be less extreme than with IDDM. The only sign may be a high blood glucose level (hyperglycaemia) picked up on routine testing by your doctor.

NIDDM usually develops in people over the age of 40. It accounts for about 75 per cent of all cases. There is often a family history of diabetes.

A number of factors may influence the development of NIDDM, most importantly:

Family history, age, overweight, stress, alcohol abuse and inactivity.

With this type of diabetes, the pancreas makes some insulin, but not enough. Alternatively, excess body fat stops the insulin from carrying glucose into the body's cells.

Treatment for NIDDM is either simply a healthy diet and exercise, or a combination of these two plus tablets. **Both approaches increase the effectiveness of the insulin your body produces**. For the overweight person with this type of diabetes, losing weight is the best treatment.

Some people with NIDDM who control their diabetes by diet alone may still need insulin at some time in their life; for instance, during periods of illness or after surgery.

Diabetes tablets and how they work
Diabetes tablets (oral hypoglycaemic agents) help lower your blood glucose level.
They don't contain insulin, but help the body make more insulin or help you to use the insulin you have more effectively.

What happens if diabetes remains uncontrolled?

If your blood glucose level remains high or fluctuates excessively over a period, this may damage the blood vessels that supply your eyes, kidneys, heart and other organs and nerves, especially in your legs and feet. Learning how to manage your diabetes and to achieve good control is the best way to help avoid these fluctuations.

MANAGING DIABETES TODAY

Essentially, good management of diabetes focuses on three major approaches:

- Diet alone

- Diet and diabetes tablets

- Diet and insulin injections

Exactly which approach is most beneficial for you will depend on what type of diabetes you have, your weight, age and your blood glucose level.

There are three other important guidelines which will keep you fit and in good health:

- **Regular exercise** makes an important difference to diabetes and to your sense of well-being in general.

- **Regular monitoring of your blood or urine glucose levels** helps you to get to know your body and how it is coping with diabetes. It shows you the effect food, exercise and medication have on your blood glucose level (BGL), and helps you to adjust them as necessary.

- **Regular visits to your doctor, dietitian and/or diabetes specialist nurse** — your partners in ongoing health care.

What can diet do for diabetes?

Food is important in keeping healthy, whether we have diabetes or not. However, most people don't pay enough attention to their basic nutritional needs. Diabetes highlights the importance of a well-balanced eating pattern.

If you have diabetes, there are three important benefits from a nutritionally sound diet:

- Firstly, it helps you to achieve and maintain good control of your blood glucose level.

- Secondly, it helps you to regulate your body weight.

- Thirdly, it helps to prevent or delay onset of any long-term problems linked with diabetes.

THE GOLDEN RULES FOR DIABETICS

The way to keep healthy now and in the future is to follow these Golden Rules:

- **Understand your diabetes and how to manage it.** Ask questions. Don't be shy or worry that you seem 'stupid' or are being a nuisance. No matter how 'silly' your question, ask it. And keep on asking until you are entirely satisfied that you understand your diabetes and know what to do to manage it. If, like so many people, you tend to go blank when seeing the dietitian, doctor or diabetes specialist nurse, sit down before your visit and write out all your questions and concerns. Take your list with you and go through it item by item.

These people are often busy and, if you need extra time, make an appointment for a less busy time. Alternatively, ask for a double appointment. Make sure you understand exactly what the prescribed treatment is supposed to do, and exactly how to follow it. You can also take a parent, friend or partner to help you to remember what was said.

- **Keep your blood glucose level under control.** The best way of doing this is to eat sensibly, exercise regularly and take your medication correctly.

- **If you are overweight, make losing weight a goal.** If you are slim, stay slim. There is no magic to losing weight. Basically, you need to make sure that you eat fewer kilojoules (calories) than your body burns up. You probably know whether you are eating too much, but if you are unsure of how to cut down on kilojoules (calories) without losing out on good nutrition, look at the sample meal plans in this book.

  NOTE: 1 calorie = 4.2 kilojoules (kJ)

  Once you are slim, keep a careful watch on what you eat; it's all a matter of balance. You need to eat just enough to fuel your body through its normal daily routine, so concentrate on those things that provide your body with enough nutrients to keep it functioning perfectly. Remember, you can do this and still enjoy varied and tasty meals.

- **Be as physically active as possible,** keeping in mind your age, general health and your ability to exercise. Remember too that exercise lowers your blood sugar level and that this will always need to be balanced with enough carbohydrate to keep your blood sugar levels normal. This is not a call to becoming a super-athlete; simply by taking a brisk walk around the block twice a day you can keep fit. You may prefer to swim a few laps, play bowls or tennis, ride your bicycle or walk to the local shops instead of driving. But whatever exercise you choose, and whatever level of physical activity you find most comfortable, make it a regular part of your life. The benefits are immense.

UNDERSTANDING THE PRINCIPLES OF GOOD NUTRITION

Food is an important part of life — it is a necessity and it should also be a pleasure. Diabetes need not change either of these aspects.

What we eat is a very individual matter. It's one of those areas where personal choice is allowed a wide expression. How you feel at any particular moment, your tastes, your cultural background and lifestyle all have an effect.

The enjoyment we get from food should be matched by its value as a source of nourishment. It's the sort of thing we all are becoming more aware of, but may well ignore. However, when you develop diabetes, you have the opportunity to reappraise what you eat and improve your eating habits with immediate and significant benefits.

Foods provide different textures, flavours, colours and nutritional value, and eating a variety will ensure the best combination for good health. The nutrients in food include protein, fat, carbohydrate, vitamins, minerals, fibre and water, all of which are essential for continued good health. It may be of help to know what these different nutrients do, and why they are vital.

PROTEIN

- Protein is an important part of all body tissues, enzymes, hormones and the immune system.

- You need protein for body growth and repair.

- Protein has only a small role as a body fuel.

- The richest sources are meat, poultry, fish, seafood, dairy products, eggs, nuts, seeds and pulses. You don't have to eat huge quantities of protein to enjoy its benefits.

FAT

- Provides fuel to keep the body working.

- Plays an important part in insulating and protecting the body's organs and other tissues.

- Transports other nutrients around the body.

- Major sources of fat include butter, margarine, oils, meat, milk, cream and cheese. You need very small amounts of fat daily to perform the above important tasks.

CARBOHYDRATE

- Is the most important fuel source for all body tissues, especially the brain.

- Plays an important part in many body functions.

- Carbohydrate comes in two main forms — sugars and starches. Sugars are found naturally in fruit, milk and honey, and are added as sweeteners to many foods such as confectionery, cakes, soft drinks and jams. You find starches in breads, cereals, grains, vegetables and pulses.

VITAMINS

- Help the body to produce fuel from carbohydrate, fat and protein.

- Work in combination with protein in growth and repair of body tissues.

- Play an essential part in body functions.

There are two types:

- Water-soluble vitamins — all B vitamins and Vitamin C — which are found widely in foods including fruits, vegetables, cereals, milk and meat.

- Fat-soluble vitamins — A, D, E and K — which are found in animal fats such as butter, other dairy products, meat, vegetable oils and margarines, wholegrain products, nuts and seeds.

MINERALS

- Form a major part of bones, teeth and body fluids such as blood.

- Play an essential part in body functions such as heart beat, muscle contraction, and in nervous system and fluid balance.

- Occur widely in foods such as meat and fish, milk and cheese, fruits, vegetables and cereal products.

FIBRE

- This used to be called roughage and is the part of plant foods which is not broken down by the digestive juices in the small intestine.

- It has several tasks, including keeping the digestive tract in good shape. In other words, it keeps our bowels functioning regularly.

- It also helps to fill the stomach, satisfy our appetite and limit over-eating.

- Fibre keeps us satisfied after a meal, and delays the onset of hunger by slowing both digestion and the rate at which our body absorbs nutrients. In particular, from the point of view of a person with diabetes, it slows the rate of absorption of carbohydrate from the gut, thereby helping to control your blood glucose level.

- Fibre is invaluable in your diet. Eat lots of it. Good sources of fibre include wholegrain breads and cereals, fruits, vegetables and pulses.

WATER

- Water is an essential part of every body function. About two-thirds of the body is water.

- We lose between 1 and 3 litres (1³/4 and 5 pints) of water every day through the lungs and in sweat, urine and faeces. The body can survive only for a few days without replacing this loss.

- Water is still the best drink for health. Don't wait until you're thirsty. Drink 1.5 – 2 litres (2³/4 – 3¹/2 pints, 6 – 8 cups) of fluid (tea, water, coffee, artificially sweetened soft drinks) a day, and you will feel the benefit.

Food as a fuel source

Food is the energy source or fuel that keeps our bodies working. The energy supplied by any food is measured in kilojoules (or calories). Energy comes from three particular nutrients in our food. We have ranked them in order of importance: carbohydrate; then fat; lastly, protein.

Alcohol provides concentrated energy, but it isn't usually considered a nutrient and certainly isn't essential. Carbohydrate and protein supply 17 kilojoules (4 calories) per gram; alcohol supplies 29 kilojoules (7 calories) per gram, and fat 37 kilojoules (9 calories) per gram.

GUIDELINES FOR CHOOSING FOOD

A good guide for choosing a healthy diet is set out below. Follow these guidelines and you will be on the way to managing your health and your diabetes. The first five are particularly important if you have diabetes:

- Eat plenty of bread and cereals (preferably wholegrain), pulses, vegetables and fruit.

- Limit your sugar intake.

- Limit your fat intake.

- Limit the amount of alcohol you drink.

- Control your weight.

But don't ignore the rest. Here they are:

- Choose a nutritious diet from a variety of foods.

- Cut back on salt.

- Encourage breast feeding.

- Drink plenty of water.

In this section, we will explain why these guidelines are important to you.

EAT PLENTY OF BREADS AND CEREALS (ESPECIALLY WHOLEGRAIN), PULSES, FRUIT AND VEGETABLES

These foods offer a number of benefits, and should make up the bulk of your diet. They contain plenty of carbohydrate and fibre, vitamins and minerals and, if you eat them regularly, they will actually help to control your diabetes. They will also help you to control your weight because they are satisfying and bulky.

Important: Try to include at least two or three portions of high-carbohydrate, high-fibre food (as shown next) in every meal. If you are young and active, your carbohydrate requirements may be much higher and you may find that you need high carbohydrate snacks in your eating plan to ensure that you have enough carbohydrate-releasing energy in your system all through the day.

CEREALS

Include bread, biscuits, breakfast cereals, rice, wheat, barley, oats, buckwheat, rye, pasta (such as spaghetti and noodles). For example:

2 slices of bread or 1 bread roll
4 – 6 dry biscuits
90 g (3 oz, 1 cup) of cereal
100 g (3 1/2 oz, 3/4 cup) of pasta
100 g (3 1/2 oz, 1/2 cup) of cooked rice

PULSES

Include dried beans (such as red kidney beans, borlotti, white, black-eyed, lima, haricot, cannellini, baked beans and soy beans), peas (such as split peas and chick-peas) and lentils. For example:

170 g (6 oz, 3/4 cup) cooked

VEGETABLES

Starchy vegetables include potatoes, sweet potatoes, pumpkin, parsnip, beetroot, sweetcorn and yams. For example:

150 – 170 g (5 – 6 oz, 3/4 – 1 cup) cooked

Vegetables, other than the starchy ones listed above, are low in carbohydrate, but high in fibre, and are a particularly rich source of minerals and vitamins. You should include them in your daily diet together with starchy vegetables.

FRUIT

Include all varieties. For example:

1 large piece of fruit or the equivalent

200 g (7 oz, 1 cup) stewed fruit

Some fruits are lower in carbohydrate than others. The list on page 201 will prove a useful guide.

All about carbohydrate and fibre-rich food

Carbohydrate is important for you if you have diabetes. After all, carbohydrate breaks down into glucose, and balancing your blood glucose level is a vital part of your management.

It is essential that you understand the difference between refined (simple) sugars, such as sugar itself, and complex (or unrefined) carbohydrate, such as cereals and breads.

Refined sugars, especially if eaten on their own and in large amounts, are absorbed quickly from the digestive tract into the bloodstream, causing a rapid rise in blood glucose levels. This can make control of diabetes more difficult.

Complex carbohydrate needs to be broken down in your digestive system and, especially when combined with fibre, releases glucose into the bloodstream in a controlled and sustained way. You get the energy you need, but you avoid surges in your blood glucose level. This is the best type of carbohydrate to include in your diet.

Once you understand this simple difference, you have taken a major step towards making good food choices for your diabetes.

FIBRE

As mentioned earlier, fibre is important in helping to control your blood glucose level. To maximize your fibre intake:

- Choose wholegrain/wholemeal breakfast cereals. For the best choices see page 38.

- Replace white rice and pastas with brown rice and wholemeal pastas. You'll be delighted with how tasty they are.

- Use more pulses in your cooking. Add them to soups, casseroles, salads, savoury dishes and even to dips.

- Make sure you eat vegetables every day (including the starchy ones). Use them in salads, soups, meat dishes and so on.

- Include at least two to three pieces of fruit in your daily eating plan. Preferably eat them fresh rather than cooked, and don't drink more than one **small** glass of fruit juice per day, as this is low in fibre.

- Leave vegetables and fruit unpeeled where possible, for maximum fibre.

LIMIT YOUR SUGAR INTAKE

An enormous number of the processed foods we eat contain added sugars. You will find sugar in many forms, some obvious, some less so, in many of the foods you buy such as biscuits, some cereals, canned fruit, soft drinks, sweets and chocolates. Sugars are high in kilojoules (calories) but often are low in other nutrients. This means that they can add to your weight without providing any useful nourishment. The small amount of sugar present in savoury foods is fine to have and does not significantly affect the blood glucose levels.

Diabetes does not mean a total ban on sugars. You can eat small amounts as part of meals and in combination with high-fibre foods without making your blood glucose levels rise excessively. In practice, this means that a scrape of jam on wholemeal toast or a little sugar used in your whole-meal cake recipe will do no harm.

You can also train your palate to prefer far less sugar than we have become accustomed to in our western diet.

Hints to help you cut down on sugars

- Always check product labels. Read *Making Sense of Food Labels* (page 28).

- Avoid sugar in tea, coffee or other beverages.

- Buy solid-pack unsweetened canned fruit, fruit packed in water or natural juice, or artificially sweetened canned fruit instead of fruit canned in syrups.

- Water is still the best thirst quencher. But low-joule (low-calorie) soft drinks, flavoured mineral waters and cordials are also readily available.

- If you want flavoured jellies, use the low-joule (low-calorie) products.

- If you like jam, marmalade or honey on your toast or bread, have some, but limit it to a scrape, or try the reduced-sugar, pure fruit jams.

- In your cooking, look for recipes with very little or no sugar, fructose or honey. Our recipes will give you a guide as to just how little sugar or sweetness you need to make food delicious. Remember, too, that fruit is a good source of sweetness. In many of our recipes you will see that we use fruit and fruit juices in recipes which traditionally are made with sugar.

- Try the very low-fat diet yoghurts or make your own by combining low-fat plain yoghurt and your choice of fresh or stewed fruits.

LIMIT YOUR FAT INTAKE

Fat is a taste-enhancer, and we have become used to eating far too much of it. Not only do we use it knowingly by frying foods or by ladling on the cream; we also eat a great deal of fat unknowingly in processed foods. It is sobering to realize that a 100 g (3½ oz) packet of potato crisps contains 40 per cent fat and 2385 kJ (570 cal) and that a plain, unsweetened shop-bought biscuit may have as much as 20 per cent fat and 262 kJ (63 cal).

Because fat is the most concentrated form of energy we eat, there is a danger that a diet high in fats will add unnecessary kilojoules (calories). It may well lead to you putting on weight, which anyone with diabetes ought to avoid.

Heart and circulation problems are often associated with a diet high in fats. Reduce your fat intake, and this may reduce your chances of developing such problems.

Remember that eating too much fat may have a direct effect on insulin activity in your body, causing an increase in your blood glucose level.

Just as you don't have to give up sweetness in your foods, you don't have to give up fats altogether. It is important, however, that you limit your intake. Cutting back begins in the kitchen, and continues at the table.

Hints to help you use less fat

- Use the absolute minimum oil or fat in cooking. If possible, don't use any added fat at all.

- When you must use fat, use a brush to spread a thin layer of fat on to your pan, or use a cooking spray.

- Grill or roast meat on a rack to allow the fat to drip away.

- For soups and casseroles, drop meat into boiling water to seal it rather than browning it in fat or oil.

- Choose a low-fat spread, preferably one based on monounsaturated or polyunsaturated fats, and use sparingly. If you prefer to use ordinary butter or margarine, use sparingly. Use cottage cheese or a scrape of low-fat soft cheese as a spread instead.

- Use 'no-oil', 'low-oil', or 'low-joule' (low-calorie) salad dressings instead of oily ones or mayonnaise. Better still, use lemon juice or vinegar with herbs to add zest to your salads. Turn to our *Dressings* section (page 158) for ideas.

- Learn to use fresh or dried herbs and spices to add flavour to food instead of butter or oil.

- Avoid adding oil or fat to vegetables during or after preparation. For instance, when you mash potato or other vegetables, don't add butter or margarine. Use low-fat milk. Wrap your vegetables in foil with herbs, or try dry-baking them in the oven in their own skins.

- If you like soured cream as a vegetable dressing, use cottage cheese or low-fat plain yoghurt instead.

- Use our recipe for Creamy Whipped Topping (see page 163) instead of cream on desserts.

- Try using low-fat alternatives such as skimmed or semi-skimmed milk.

- Choose leaner cuts of meat and trim off any fat. Remove the skin from poultry as this contains a lot of fat.

Our recipes reflect our recommendations; we use fat, where necessary, but sparingly. The recipes will convince you that you can eat wonderful, nutritious food and still cut down on fat.

Protein foods

Protein foods often contain fat, so be aware of this when you make choices. Consider the following:

MEAT, POULTRY, FISH

Many people eat far too much protein food; at the same time, protein is important to a healthy eating plan and you should include some every day. However, you only need one or two small portions of protein daily. By a small portion, we mean about 90 g (3 oz) of cooked meat or fish. To give you some idea of what this means, 90 g (3 oz) of steak is a piece about the size of an average hamburger patty. If in doubt, weigh your meats or fish, or ask your butcher or fishmonger to weigh them for you.

When choosing protein foods, select those which are lower in fat, such as:

- **Lean** beef, veal, pork or lamb
- Chicken or turkey without skin
- Fish and seafood
- Game meat such as rabbit and venison

To be classified as lean, meat should have minimal visible fat marbled through it, and you should trim off any fat around the meat **before** you cook it.

EGGS

Eggs are a good source of protein. They are low in fat, although the yolk is rich in cholesterol. Unless you have a high cholesterol level, you can eat three or four eggs a week.

PULSES

Pulses are excellent as a source of protein and have the added advantage of being low in fat. They make an ideal alternative or addition to meat dishes. Because they are also rich in carbohydrate and fibre, you should eat plenty of them. 170 g (6 oz, 3/4 cup) of cooked pulses provides about the same amount of protein as a 90 g (3 oz) portion of meat.

NUTS AND SEEDS

Nuts and seeds — and products made from them, such as peanut butter and tahini — are a valuable source of protein. But they are high in fat, so eat them in moderation.

MILK AND MILK PRODUCTS

Remember that while standard milk and dairy products are high in fat, there are many low-fat products available and you would do well to use them:

- Skimmed or low-fat milks

- Skimmed or low-fat yoghurts

- Skimmed or low-fat cheeses

When choosing low-fat cheeses, preferably choose those with less than 20 per cent fat. Also try to avoid eating any form of cream — save this for special occasions and, even then, use it in small amounts.

If you really enjoy ice-cream, then have some occasionally in small amounts. Nearly all ice-creams and ice-confections are high in fat and/or sugar. This is true not only for standard ice-cream, but also for low-fat and carbohydrate-modified ice-creams, soft ices and ice confections such as tofu, frozen yoghurts and gelati. The low-fat, artificially sweetened substitutes for slimmers and diabetics are useful to keep in the freezer to have in moderate quantities to cool off on hot days.

A special note on milk

Dairy products are important sources of protein and calcium. Women, particularly, should be aware of the value of dairy products in helping to protect them from osteoporosis (loss of calcium from your bones). Calcium, of course, plays a vital part in good bone health.

Adults should include 300 ml (1/2 pint) or the equivalent in dairy products in their daily diet. Children, adolescents, women over 50, and women who are pregnant or breast-feeding should double this. They should include 600 ml (1 pint) of milk or the equivalent in dairy products in their daily diet.

*The following each contain **about** the **same quantity** of calcium:*

100 ml (3 1/2 fl oz) milk

100 ml (3 1/2 fl oz) yoghurt

15 g (1/2 oz) piece of cheese

LIMIT THE AMOUNT OF ALCOHOL YOU DRINK

Alcoholic drinks are high in kilojoules (calories), which means that they can cause weight gain. They can also react with diabetes tablets or insulin, causing a drop in your blood glucose levels. It is therefore important to have something to eat with your drink or shortly afterwards.

Having diabetes does not mean that you cannot drink alcohol at all. It simply means moderation and good sense. If you drink alcohol, then we recommend that you do not drink more than one or two standard alcoholic drinks a day. By a 'standard' drink we mean a small glass of beer, a glass of wine or a 30 ml (1 oz) nip of spirits such as whisky, vodka or gin.

If you are drinking beer or lager, choose the ordinary varieties (preferably those with an alcohol content of less than 5 per cent). Low-sugar (Pils) beers tend to be high in alcohol and are best avoided.

Low-alcohol beers and lagers are useful, especially if you are driving. However, it is important to check that your drink is virtually alcohol-free and not just reduced in alcohol. The alcohol-free drinks tend to have a high sugar content and should be treated like a sugary drink.

A note about mixers

When using mixers, be aware that all the standard soft drinks contain significant amounts of refined sugar, and we do not advise their use. But low-joule (low-calorie) mixers can be used freely. Most of them are sweetened with artificial sweeteners so use:

- *Water*
- *Soda water*
- *Unflavoured mineral water*
- *Low-joule (low-calorie) tonics, dry ginger ale, bitter lemon, cola-flavoured drinks and lemonade*

Unsweetened fruit juice and milk contain carbohydrate and are useful mixers where no better source of carbohydrate is available, such as a slice of bread or a dry biscuit.

Most importantly, don't drink alcohol on an empty stomach. **Always** eat some starchy food when you drink, for example, dry biscuits with your whisky, a meal with your wine.

If you are taking diabetes medication, and you drink alcohol without having carbohydrate, your blood glucose level may drop too low, leading to hypoglycaemia or 'hypo' which can be serious and require urgent treatment. On page 42 we tell you more about hypoglycaemia, and how to prevent and treat it. You will also find more information on alcohol on page 202.

CONTROL YOUR WEIGHT

Being overweight makes diabetes more difficult to control. The extra body fat alters the cell receptor sites so that they are unable to accept the combination of insulin and glucose. As a result, blood glucose level remains too high.

Fortunately, once you lose excess weight, the receptor sites are reactivated, allowing insulin to be taken up effectively so that your blood glucose level can be controlled without medication or with minimal amounts of injected insulin or tablets.

If you are overweight, losing weight is the key to good diabetes control, and should be a priority. It will also benefit your overall health. Check the following chart to see whether you need to maintain or lose weight.

TABLE OF ACCEPTABLE WEIGHTS-FOR-HEIGHTS 2,5 cm = 1 in   1 kg = 2,2 lb

Height cm	Weight kg	Height cm	Weight kg	Height cm	Weight kg
140	39–49	158	50–62	176	62–77
142	40–50	160	51–64	178	63–79
144	41–52	162	52–66	180	65–81
146	43–53	164	54–67	182	66–83
148	44–55	166	55–69	184	68–85
150	45–56	168	56–71	186	69–86
152	46–58	170	58–72	188	71–88
154	47–59	172	59–74	190	72–90
156	48–61	174	61–76		

Height (cm) – without shoes   *Body weight (kg) – in light clothing without shoes*

Whether you need to maintain or lose weight, the guidelines given in this book will help you achieve your goal. If you need to lose weight, you will have to reduce your kilojoule (calorie) intake.

By limiting your fat and sugar intake, and having more foods high in carbohydrate and fibre, you should be able to control your weight and still eat enough to satisfy your appetite.

While you are losing weight, it is important to maintain your health by eating regular meals that supply all your nutritional needs. Avoid crash diets and quick solutions – they offer no long term benefits. Developing a healthy eating pattern over a period will help you to achieve and maintain a lower weight.

***Remember**, in your quest for better health:*
- *Eat regular meals each day*
- *Include plenty of wholegrain bread, cereals, pulses, vegetables and fruit every day*
- *Cut down on fats, concentrated sugars and alcohol*
- *Reduce your weight if you are overweight; if you are slim, keep that way*
- *Eating should be a pleasure; make sure your meals have plenty of flavour and texture*

Foreground: Ginger Pears, next Mixed Berry Salad with Lemon Cream, and Lemon Delight above. Mocha Mousse served in the tall glass.

ON THE SHELVES

ARTIFICIAL SWEETENERS

Wherever possible, enjoy the natural sweetness of food. But if you must have added sweetness, you can use the many alternatives to sugar available on the market.

Artificial sweeteners are available in different physical forms: tablets, granulated or liquid. They also have different tastes and sweetening capacity, so it would be advisable to shop around to find a brand which suits your particular needs.

The three main uses of sweeteners are:

- As table-top sweeteners, for example, sprinkling over cereals or fruit
- As an ingredient in food
- As an ingredient in beverages.

Unfortunately, artificial sweeteners (even the granulated ones) for use in the home do not add bulk to a recipe in the way that sugar can, and they are, therefore, not suitable for all baking purposes. Sweeteners are used spoon for spoon like sugar, for example, 5 ml (1 tsp) of sugar would be replaced by 5 ml (1 tsp) of granulated sweetener. However, as they are lighter than sugar, in most cases about 30 g (1 oz) of granulated sweetener would replace 300 g (10 oz) of sugar.

Similarly, 5 ml (1 tsp) of liquid sweetener would generally provide the same sweetness as 60 g (2 oz) of sugar, contributing only one-tenth of its calories. Tablet sweeteners each have the sweetening strength of 5 ml (1 tsp) of sugar. So if you usually have 10 ml (2 tsp) of sugar in a cup of tea, you would need to use around 2 tablets to give the same sweetness.

Artificial sweeteners which have negligible kilojoules (calories) include:

ASPARTAME. It was discovered by chance when a scientist was researching ulcer drugs. It is marketed under various brand names and we have used it in many of our recipes. It is also used to sweeten a host of commercially prepared foods and beverages.

Because it tends to break down under high heat or during lengthy cooking, aspartame is not suitable for cooking or baking, unless you add it at the end of the process. This is not always possible, for instance in baking, and so other sweeteners should be used.

Aspartame is 180 times sweeter than sugar, dissolves in liquid (making it useful as a sweetener in tea and coffee), and has no unpleasant aftertaste.

CYCLAMATE. This too was a chance discovery. In 1937 a scientist tasted sweetness on his cigarette after he had put it down accidentally on some white powder. When he checked, he discovered the sweetener cyclamate.

Foreground: Orange and Cucumber Salad, to the right Spinach Ravioli with Fresh Tomato Sauce, in the centre a spectacular Crab Quiche, with sliced Quick Wholemeal Bread.

Cyclamate is 30 times sweeter than sugar. It enjoyed considerable popularity for many years, but then became the focus of safety issues. In 1969 it was banned in the USA and the United Kingdom when it was implicated in possible liver and kidney damage in laboratory animals. However, the Carcinogen Assessment Group in the United States determined that cyclamate does not cause cancer in humans. Pending further research into other possible side-effects, cyclamate remains banned in the United States although it is widely available in the rest of the world, including Australia.

It is soluble and therefore useful as a sweetener in hot and cold drinks. It does not have as strong an aftertaste as saccharin, and does not lose its sweetening qualities when cooked.

SACCHARIN. The oldest of the artificial sweeteners, it was discovered in 1879 and went into commercial use in the early 1900s. It is 300 times sweeter than sugar, but up to one in four people notice a bitter or metallic aftertaste in foods sweetened with it. By mixing saccharin with cyclamate the taste can be improved. Saccharin is soluble and therefore useful as a sweetener; however, it is best added as late as possible in the cooking process to limit the development of any unpleasant, bitter aftertaste.

How much?

In the United Kingdom the Government has set an Acceptable Daily Intake (ADI) for saccharin of up to 5 mg per kg body weight. For an average adult this would be the equivalent of around 30 teaspoons of granulated saccharin-based sweetener or about 25 saccharin-based tablets in any one day.

This is more saccharin than most people would consume. However, we would like to reassure people with diabetes that large safety margins are used when calculating ADIs and if this quantity was exceeded on the odd occasion, it would not be a cause for concern.

If you are a regular 'heavy user' of saccharin (for example having more than 15 cups of beverages a day sweetened with 10 ml (2 tsp) of saccharin), it might be advisable to vary the type of sweetener used and to reduce total sweetener consumption.

For aspartame the ADI is 40 mg/kg body weight (it would be very difficult to take more than this in any one day). Acesulfame K has an ADI of 9 mg/kg body weight.

Obviously it is sensible to limit the total daily intake of artificial sweeteners to reasonable quantities as with any food or drink. If possible, choose a variety of products which offer more than one type of sweetener and vary the brand you use at home from time to time. Bear in mind that the taste is individual.

Artificial sweeteners supplying kilojoules (calories) include:

SORBITOL. It is manufactured commercially from glucose obtained from natural sources such as fruits. It is absorbed slowly into the bloodstream and, therefore, does not cause a major increase in blood glucose level, although it supplies as many kilojoules (calories) as other sugars. Because of the kilojoules (calories) it contains, we would recommend that you avoid or limit its use. Be aware, too, that more than 30 g (1 oz) of sorbitol taken in a single day may have a laxative effect.

MANNITOL. This is a sugar alcohol made from mannose which is found in seaweed and some other natural products. It is approximately half as sweet as sugar and may have a mild laxative effect if you take more than 30 g (1 oz) a day. It contributes only about 8 kilojoules (2 calories) per gram because it is poorly absorbed.

FRUCTOSE. Occurring naturally in fruits and honey, it can be purchased as a white powder which is slightly sweeter than sugar, but contains the same amount of energy per weight.

Fructose used to be recommended for use in baked goods because it did not cause a significant rise in blood sugar levels. However, recent studies have shown that the effect of sucrose on blood sugars may have been over-estimated and that small amounts of sugar as part of an overall healthy diet (high-fibre, low-fat, low-sugar) would have no significant effect on the blood sugar levels either.

There is no reason why people with diabetes and their carers cannot use fructose for baking, but it is expensive and the result may not be as good.

LACTOSE. Lactose or milk sugar is frequently used as a bulking agent to produce powdered artificial sweeteners which resemble sugar in appearance. It contributes the same amount of kilojoules (calories) as any other sugars. Use this type of sweetener with caution.

Other intense sweeteners include sucralose, thaumatin and alitame; other bulk sweeteners include xylitol, maltifol, isomalt and hydrogenated glucose syrup.

Read the labels of your sweeteners carefully. Many are made from combinations of sweeteners, or are bulked up with agents such as lactose. The following table sets out the various artificial sweeteners and their kilojoule (calorie) counts.

Tips and traps when using artificial sweeteners

- Artificial sweeteners are much sweeter than sugar, so you only need a small amount.

- Some people's taste-buds are very sensitive to these products, and they describe a lingering bitter or metallic aftertaste. Using a different sweetener or using less of the product may help you to overcome this.

- Cyclamate and saccharin develop a bitter taste when boiled, particularly when cooked with fruit. Always add these sweeteners after the fruit has been cooked and has cooled. Where food is not boiled, for example, when baking an egg custard, the sweetener can be added before cooking.

- Aspartame loses its sweetness with prolonged storage in liquids. For example, soft drinks sweetened with aspartame do not store well.

- Aspartame loses its sweetness when heated and is not suitable for dishes which require heating.

- Some sweeteners are mixed with other sugars such as lactose and glucose to reduce the concentration of their sweetness, and to enable you to sprinkle them. This adds kilojoules (calories), so use them sparingly.

- Some products are advertised as sugar-free, but if you read the label, you will see that they contain quite large amounts of sweeteners such as sorbitol and fructose.

'DIABETIC' OR 'CARBOHYDRATE-MODIFIED' PRODUCTS

You will find a great number of foods targeted at people with diabetes. On the whole, they are expensive and we regard their use as unnecessary. Furthermore, a number of them are high in kilojoules (calories). As long as you make a point of learning about what ordinary foods contain, and the nutrient value of foods, you should need few, if any, diabetic products as these contain the same amount of fat and are not significantly lower in kilojoules (calories) than the non-diabetic counterparts.

Some common diabetic foods:

- Diabetic chocolates and confectionery diabetic jams (carbohydrate-modified), diabetic ice-creams (carbohydrate-modified), diabetic biscuits, diabetic chutneys, pickles and sauces. The ordinary varieties are acceptable in small amounts.

LOW-JOULE (LOW-CALORIE) PRODUCTS

These products are marketed for people who want to lose weight. As such, they are suitable for people with diabetes and you can use them freely. Here are some of them:

- Low-joule (low-calorie) jams, confectionery and jellies, low-joule (low-calorie) soft drinks and cordials, low-oil or no-oil salad dressings.

'SUGAR-FREE' PRODUCTS

Foods labelled 'sugar-free' are only free of added sucrose, and they should not be confused with low-joule (low-calorie) products. Some are high in naturally occurring sugars such as fructose, lactose, grape juice, apple concentrate and pear juice. The kilojoule (calorie) value of these products can be as high as standard sweetened products; you should use them sparingly.

If you are still uncertain whether a product is suitable, read the label carefully and, if it appears high in these sugars, ask your dietitian for advice (see the next section for information on understanding labels).

MAKING SENSE OF FOOD LABELS

Many commercial foods which you can buy at the supermarket contain a lot of sugar and/or fat and may be low in fibre, making them unsuitable for you. But how do you know which ones they are?

There are now food-labelling laws in most countries which state that all ingredients in a product must appear on a label, listed in order of quantity. This means that the ingredient used in the greatest amount is listed first, and that used in the smallest amount is listed last.

For example, let us look at a product label including the following ingredients: **Wheat flour, oats, beef fat, malt extract, sultanas, flavouring, salt.**

There is more wheat flour in this product than anything else, and less salt.

To help you to decide which products are suitable or unsuitable, we have listed some of the names used for fat, sugar and fibre:

FAT		SUGAR		FIBRE
beef fat	oil	apple concentrate	lactose	bran
beef tallow	shortening	brown sugar	malt	oatbran
butter fat	soya bean oil	corn syrup	malt extract	ricebran
coconut cream	vegetable oil	dextrose	maltose	rolled oats
coconut oil		glucose	mannitol	wheatgerm
copha		fructose	molasses	wheatmeal
corn oil		golden syrup	pear concentrate	wholegrain
cottonseed oil		grape concentrate	sorbitol	wholemeal
lard		honey	sucrose	
margarine		invert sugar	treacle	
			xylitol	

Reading labels provides valuable information, but it is not always as straightforward as it looks. You need to know how to interpret the information so you can make wise choices.

Here are some examples of labels used in different countries:

NUTRITION INFORMATION

	per 100 g	per 37.5 g serving
Energy	1453 kJ	545 kJ
	342 kcal	128 kcal
Protein	11.2 g	4.2 g
Carbohydrate	65.8 g	24.7 g
of which sugars	4.9 g	1.8 g
Fat	2.7 g	1.0 g
of which saturates	0.5 g	0.2 g
Fibre	12.9 g	4.8 g
of which soluble	4.0 g	1.5 g
insoluble	8.9 g	3.3 g
Sodium	0.3 g	0.1 g

Vitamins	per 100 g	% RDA per 37.5 g serving
Niacin	8.2 mg	17%
Riboflavin (B2)	0.7 mg	17%
Thiamine (B1)	0.5 mg	17%
Iron	5.4 mg	17%

An average serving of two Weetabix (37.5 g) will provide at least 17% of the recommended daily amount (RDA) for the average adult of the vitamins and iron listed. This pack contains twelve 2-biscuit servings.

Weetabix Ingredients:

Whole Wheat, Malt Extract, Sugar, Salt, Niacin, Iron, Riboflavin (B_2), Thiamin (B_1).

At first glance you might think this produce is unsuitable because sugar appears as the third ingredient. However, this small amount would have no significant effect on the blood sugar levels.

Baked beans in tomato sauce vegetarian ingredients: Navy beans, tomato purée, sugar, thickener (modified cornflour), salt, food acid (260), spices, water added.

NUTRITION INFORMATION

Serving per package	6.0
Serving size	125 g

INGREDIENTS:
NAVY BEANS 50%, TOMATO PUREE, SUGAR, THICKENER (MODIFIED MAIZE STARCH), SALT, SPICES, FOOD ACID (296), NATURAL COLOURS (150, 160e) WATER ADDED.

SPC LIMITED, ANDREW FAIRLEY AVE., SHEPPARTON, VICTORIA, 3630, AUSTRALIA

	PER SERVE 125 g	PER 100 g
Energy	480 kJ	384 kJ
Protein	6.1 g	4.9 g
Fat	0.9 g	0.7 g
Carbohydrates – Total	21.5 g	17.2 g
– Sugars	5.5 g	4.4 g
Dietary Fibre	6.3 g	5.0 g
Sodium	479 mg	383 mg
Potassium	350 mg	280 mg

BETTER CEREAL CHOICES

Start your day right with cereal for breakfast. But with the great number of products available, it is difficult to know which ones to choose. Your best choices are high in fibre and low in added sugar.

To help you make a sensible choice, we have divided some of the most popular types and makes into two groups: Recommended and Not Recommended. For cereals not on the following list, read the labels and use our guidelines.

To be included in our **recommended** list, 30 g (1 oz) of cereal had to contain no more than 5 g of added sugar and at least 2.5 g or more of dietary fibre. This sugar content is equivalent to 5 ml (1 tsp) of sugar, and the fibre is approximately equal to the amount you would find in a slice of wholemeal bread.

Those which are high in sugar are not recommended. ●

Unless indicated, all products are available in Australia, New Zealand, the United Kingdom and South Africa.

Recommended	Not recommended
Allbran™	Coco Pops™
Branbuds™ *	Cross Cuts™ *
Branflakes™	Crunchy Nut Cornflakes™
Cornflakes™	Sugar Puffs™ **
Cracked Wheat™ *	Toasted Sweetened Muesli ●
Instant Porridge	
Oatbran™	● Another disadvantage of toasted
Pronutro ***	mueslis is that they are high in fat.
Puffed Wheat™	
Ready Wheats™ *	
Rice Krispies™	
Rolled oats (not the instant varieties)	
Shredded Wheat™	
Special K™ *	* Available in the United Kingdom, Australia
Sultana Bran™ *	and New Zealand
Unsweetened untoasted muesli	** Only available in the United Kingdom
Weet-a-bix™	*** Only available in South Africa
Weeties™	
Wheat Flakes™	
Jungle Oats ***	

PLANNING YOUR MEALS

We've given you the guidelines, now comes the application. What you choose and the quantity you eat will depend on your energy requirements and your weight, as well as on that very important factor, your preferences.

YOUR ENERGY NEEDS

The following chart shows approximate energy needs for people of different ages, sex and healthy weight.

If you are active your needs may be greater; if you are physically inactive your needs may be less.

Subject	Age years	Body mass kg (lb)	Energy kJ (cal)
Boys	11–15	41 (90)	12 200 (2 920)
	15–18	61 (134)	12 600 (3 000)
Girls	11–15	42 (92)	10 400 (2 500)
	15–18	55 (121)	9 200 (2 200)
Men	18–35		11 600 (2 775)
	35–55	70 (154)	10 400 (2 500)
	55–75		8 800 (2 100)
Women	18–35		8 400 (2 000)
	35–55	58 (128)	7 600 (1 820)
	55–75		6 400 (1 530)
Pregnant (Last six months of pregnancy)	18–35	+10 (22)	9 000 (2 150)

If you need further information or guidance discuss this with your dietitian.

YOUR CARBOHYDRATE, FAT AND PROTEIN NEEDS

The average South African gets 35 per cent of his or her energy from **carbohydrate**. A healthier percentage is 50–60 per cent.

The average intake of energy from **protein** is 20–30 per cent and should be reduced to **15–20 per cent**, while the **fat** average of 45–55 per cent energy should be reduced to **30–35 per cent**.

The following chart gives you the amount of carbohydrate, protein and fat you need to eat to meet the recommended percentage intake for varying energy levels.

YOUR CARBOHYDRATE, PROTEIN AND FAT READY RECKONER

Energy (kJ)	(cal)	Carbohydrate 50–60% (g)	Protein 15–20% (g)	Fat 30% (g)
5 000	1 200	150–165	45–60	40
5 650	1 350	170–185	50–68	45
6 300	1 500	190–205	56–75	50
6 900	1 650	205–230	61–83	55
7 550	1 800	225–250	67–90	60
8 200	1 950	245–270	72–98	65
8 800	2 100	260–290	78–105	70
9 400	2 250	280–310	83–113	78
10 000	2 400	300–330	89–120	80

MORE ABOUT CARBOHYDRATE

If you are already managing your diet, you may be doing it by various methods such as simply avoiding too much sugar and fat, or by measuring 'serves' of food which contain 10 g or 15 g of carbohydrate ('portions' or 'exchanges'). **The size of the serves does not matter provided that you follow the principles of high carbohydrate and fibre, low fat and added sugar.**

The figures for carbohydrate that you are using may differ from the ones we give, but ours reflect the latest information. If your carbohydrate level is currently low and you increase it, you **may** find that your blood glucose levels are higher for a short while. Your medication may need adjusting temporarily. Discuss this with your doctor or dietitian.

For good control of your blood glucose level, **older, inactive people** should eat **at least three or four serves of high-carbohydrate, high-fibre foods** at each of their three daily meals (45–60 grams of carbohydrate per meal).

Younger and/or **more active people** may need to eat five, six or more carbohydrate serves at each meal (at least 75 grams of carbohydrate per meal).

Remember that the high-carbohydrate, high-fibre foods include bread, cereals, pulses, vegetables and fruits. On pages 17 – 18 we have shown you approximate serve sizes. Each of the carbohydrate serves shown will give you approximately 15 grams of carbohydrate.

We have also detailed the carbohydrate content of each recipe in this book so you know how much carbohydrate you are eating at each meal. For instance, one serve of Bombay Burgers (recipe, page 85) will give you about 20 grams of carbohydrate. When you accompany this with a wholemeal roll, a green salad and a serve of fruit, you have an ideal meal containing 3–4 serves (about 60 grams) of carbohydrate. The addition of a bowl of Beef and Bean Soup (recipe, page 79) will increase this to five serves (about 75 grams) of carbohydrate.

Of course, your carbohydrate intake can be made up of half serves or double serves, depending on what suits you. Remember, the figures are only approximate, and you don't have to be precise.

Generally, we do not recommend snacking between meals for older, less active people. If you are young, active or involved in vigorous exercise, or if your medications make it necessary, you may need to include high-carbohydrate snacks in your eating plan. But remember, snacking can contribute to unnecessary kilojoules (calories) which, in turn, can lead to putting on weight.

Below we have a simple meal plan which shows you how to put into practice the information we give. The carbohydrate-rich foods have been highlighted for easy identification. The quantities of food will vary from person to person, and your weight is the best guide.

Breakfast
1 serve **wholegrain cereal** with low-fat milk
1 serve **fruit**
1-2 slices **wholemeal toast** or **rye bread** with a scrape of margarine and a topping of your choice
Lunch
2 slices **wholemeal** or **rye bread** or **bread roll** with a scrape of margarine
1 thin slice of lean red meat or chicken (no skin) or tuna or salmon or egg or low-fat cheese
plenty of salad vegetables
1-2 serves **fruit**
Dinner
1 small serve lean red or white meat or fish
2 serves **starchy vegetables** or **rice** or **pasta**
plenty of non-starchy vegetables
1 serve **fruit** and/or low-fat yoghurt
Bedtime snack
1 serve **wholemeal** or **rye bread** or **wholemeal biscuit**, and a scrape of margarine
and/or 1 cup low-fat milk as drink

This menu is, of course, rather plain, but it does show how to distribute your carbohydrate evenly through the day.

MEAL PLANS

You know your kilojoule (calorie) requirements, and how much of each of the nutrients you need daily. You also know that you should spread your carbohydrate through the day. The following pages show you how to take this information and covert it into food.

We have also given lists of foods which will give you information about food values and help you add variety and interest to your meals. You will find these on pages 199 to 202.

SAMPLE MEAL PLANS

Water, tea, coffee or other low-joule beverage may be drunk with or between meals as desired.

5000 kJ (1200 Cal)

Breakfast

- 1 serve Meg's Muesli (page 58) topped with 1 sliced banana and 100 ml (3½ fl oz) low-fat milk
- 1 slice wholemeal bread spread with 5 ml (1 tsp) margarine and topped with sliced fresh tomato and black pepper

Lunch

- 1 sandwich made with 2 slices wholemeal bread spread with 10 ml (2 tsp) peanut butter and filled with chopped celery and lettuce
- 1 apple
- 2 mandarins

Dinner

- 1 serve Meatballs in Tomato Sauce (page 101) accompanied by ½ cup cooked brown rice
- 1 serve Vegetables Julienne (page 141)
- 1 serve Mocha Mousse (page 179)

Nutritional Data

Energy & nutrients: 5168 kJ (1234 Cal), 154 g carbohydrate, 74 g protein, 38 g fat
Energy ratio: 48% carbohydrate, 24% protein, 27% fat
Carbohydrate distribution: 47 g breakfast, 46 g lunch, 50 g dinner, 12 g from extra milk

6300 kJ (1500 Cal)

Breakfast

- 1 serve Meg's Muesli (page 58) topped with 1 sliced banana and 100 ml (3½ fl oz) low-fat milk
- 1 slice wholemeal bread spread with 1 tsp margarine and topped with sliced fresh tomato and black pepper
- 1 slice wholemeal toast spread with 1 tsp margarine and Date and Fig Spread (page 60)

Lunch

- 1 sandwich made with 2 slices wholemeal bread spread with 10 ml (2 tsp) peanut butter and filled with chopped celery and lettuce
- 1 slice wholemeal bread spread with 5 ml (1 tsp) margarine and yeast extract
- 1 apple
- 2 mandarins

Dinner

- Orange Borscht Soup (page 75)
- 1 serve Meatballs in Tomato Sauce (page 101) accompanied by ½ cup cooked brown rice
- 1 serve Vegetables Julienne (page 141)
- 1 serve Mocha Mousse (page 179)

Nutritional Data

Energy & nutrients: 6368 kJ (1521 Cal), 194 g carbohydrate, 84 g protein, 48 g fat
Energy ratio: 49% carbohydrate, 23% protein, 28% fat
Carbohydrate distribution: 63 g breakfast, 57 g lunch, 63 g dinner, 12 g from extra milk

SAMPLE MEAL PLANS

Water, tea, coffee or other low-joule beverage may be drunk with or between meals as desired.

7550 kJ (1800 Cal)

Breakfast

- 1 serve Meg's Muesli (page 58) topped with 1 sliced banana and 100 ml (3 ½ fl oz) low-fat milk
- 100 g (3 ½ oz) low-fat fruit yoghurt
- 1 slice wholemeal bread spread with 5 ml (1 tsp) margarine and topped with sliced fresh tomato and black pepper

Lunch

- 1 sandwich made with 2 slices wholemeal bread spread with 10 ml (2 tsp) peanut butter and filled with chopped celery and lettuce.
- 1 sandwich made with 2 slices wholemeal bread, one spread with 5 ml (1 tsp) margarine, the second with Creamy Yoghurt Dressing (page 158) and filled with grated carrot and a sprinkling of sultanas
- 1 apple
- 2 mandarins

Dinner

- Orange Borscht Soup (page 75)
- 1 serve Meatballs in Tomato Sauce (page 101) accompanied by ½ cup cooked brown rice
- 1 serve Vegetables Julienne (page 141)
- 1 serve Mocha Mousse (page 179)

Bedtime Snack

- 1 slice wholemeal bread spread with 5 ml (1 tsp) margarine and yeast extract

Nutritional Data

Energy & nutrients: 7527 kJ (1798 Cal), 238 g carbohydrate, 95 g protein, 56 g fat
Energy ratio: 51% carbohydrate, 22% protein, 28% fat
Carbohydrate distribution: 79 g breakfast, 74 g lunch, 63 g dinner, 12 g bedtime snack, 12 g from extra milk

10000 kJ (2400 Cal)

Breakfast

- 1 serve Meg's Muesli (page 58) topped with 1 sliced banana and 100 ml (3 ½ fl oz) low-fat milk
- 100 g (3 ½ oz) low-fat fruit yoghurt
- 2 slices wholemeal bread, one spread with 5 ml (1 tsp) margarine and topped with sliced fresh tomato and black pepper, the other with 5 ml (1 tsp) margarine and Date and Fig Spread (page 60)

Morning Tea

- 1 serve wholemeal biscuits spread with 5 ml (1 tsp) margarine

Lunch

- 1 sandwich made with 2 slices wholemeal bread each spread with 5 ml (1 tsp) margarine and filled with 10 ml (2 tsp) peanut butter, chopped celery and lettuce
- 1 sandwich made with 2 slices wholemeal bread, each spread with 5 ml (1 tsp) margarine, and filled with filled with grated carrot, a sprinkling of sultanas and Creamy Yoghurt Dressing (page 158)
- 1 apple
- 2 mandarins

Afternoon Tea

- 2 peaches

Dinner

- Orange Borscht Soup (page 75)
- 1 wholemeal roll (without margarine)
- 1 serve Meatballs in Tomato Sauce (page 101)
- 1 cup cooked brown rice
- 1 serve Vegetables Julienne (page 141)
- 1 serve Mocha Mousse (page 179)
- 1 cup canned apricots (no added sugar)

Bedtime Snack

- 2 slices wholemeal bread each spread with 5 ml (1 tsp) margarine and yeast extract

Nutritional Data

Energy & nutrients: 10060 kJ (2403 Cal), 333 g carbohydrate, 114 g protein, 73 g fat
Energy ratio: 54% carbohydrate, 19% protein, 27% fat
Carbohydrate distribution: 79 g breakfast, 13 g morning tea, 73 g lunch, 14 g afternoon tea, 119 g dinner, 23 g bedtime snack, 12 g from extra milk

SAMPLE VEGETARIAN MEAL PLANS

Water, tea, coffee or other low-joule beverage may be drunk with or between meals as desired.

5000 kJ (1200 Cal)

Breakfast
- 1 serve Meg's Muesli (page 58) topped with 1 sliced banana and 100 ml (3 ½ fl oz) low-fat milk
- 1 slice wholemeal bread spread with 5 ml (1 tsp) margarine and topped with sliced fresh tomato and black pepper

Lunch
- 1 sandwich made with 2 slices wholemeal bread spread with 10 ml (2 tsp) peanut butter and filled with chopped celery and lettuce
- 1 apple
- 1 mandarin

Dinner
- 1 serve Jumping Bean Bake (page 119)
- 1 serve Tossed Salad (page 150)
- 1 serve Mocha Mousse (page 179)

Nutritional Data
Energy & nutrients: 5076 kJ (1213 Cal), 160 g carbohydrate, 68 g protein, 35 g fat
Energy ratio: 51% carbohydrate, 23% protein, 26% fat
Carbohydrate distribution: 47 g breakfast, 41 g lunch, 61 g dinner, 12 g from extra milk

6300 kJ (1500 Cal)

Breakfast
- 1 serve Meg's Muesli (page 58) topped with 1 sliced banana and 100 ml (3 ½ fl oz) low-fat milk
- 1 slice wholemeal bread spread with 5 ml (1 tsp) margarine and topped with sliced fresh tomato and black pepper
- 1 slice wholemeal toast spread with 5 ml (1 tsp) margarine and Date and Fig Spread (page 60)

Lunch
- 1 sandwich made with 2 slice wholemeal bread spread with 10 ml (2 tsp) peanut butter and filled with chopped celery and lettuce
- 1 slice wholemeal bread spread with 5 ml (1 tsp) margarine and yeast extract
- 1 apple
- 1 mandarin

Dinner
- Orange Borscht Soup (page 75) prepared with vegetable stock rather than chicken
- 1 serve Jumping Bean Bake (page 119)
- 1 serve Tossed Salad (page 150)
- 1 serve Mocha Mousse (page 179)

Nutritional Data
Energy & nutrients: 6283 kJ (1501 Cal), 201 g carbohydrate, 78 g protein, 45 g fat
Energy ratio: 52% carbohydrate, 21% protein, 27% fat
Carbohydrate distribution: 63 g breakfast, 52 g lunch, 74 g dinner, 12 g from extra milk

SAMPLE VEGETARIAN MEAL PLANS

Water, tea, coffee or other low-joule beverage may be drunk with or between meals as desired.

7550 kJ (1800 Cal)

Breakfast

- 1 serve Meg's Muesli (page 58) topped with 1 sliced banana and 100 ml (3½ fl oz) low-fat milk
- 100 g (3½ oz) low-fat fruit yoghurt
- 1 slice wholemeal bread spread with 5 ml (1 tsp) margarine and topped with sliced fresh tomato and black pepper
- 1 slice wholemeal toast spread with 5 ml (1 tsp) margarine and Date and Fig Spread (page 60)

Lunch

- 1 sandwich made with 2 slices wholemeal bread spread with 10 ml (2 tsp) peanut butter and filled with chopped celery and lettuce
- 1 sandwich made with 2 slices wholemeal bread each spread with 5 ml (1 tsp) margarine, and filled with grated carrot, a sprinkling of sultanas and Creamy Yoghurt Dressing (page 158)
- 1 apple

Dinner

- Orange Borscht Soup (page 75) prepared with vegetable stock rather than chicken
- 1 serve Jumping Bean Bake (page 119)
- 1 serve Tossed Salad (page 150)
- 1 serve Mocha Mousse (page 179)

Bedtime Snack

- 1 slice wholemeal toast spread with 5 ml (1 tsp) margarine and yeast extract

Nutritional Data

Energy & nutrients: 7572 kJ (1809 Cal), 243 g carbohydrate, 90 g protein, 56 g fat
Energy ratio: 52% carbohydrate, 20% protein, 28% fat
Carbohydrate distribution: 79 g breakfast, 68 g lunch, 74 g dinner, 12 g bedtime snack, 12 g from extra milk

10000 kJ (2400 Cal)

Breakfast

- 1 serve Meg's Muesli (page 58) topped with 1 sliced banana and 100 ml (3½ fl oz) low-fat milk
- 100 g (3½ oz) low-fat fruit yoghurt
- 2 slices wholemeal toast, one spread with 5 ml (1 tsp) margarine and topped with fresh tomato and black pepper, the other with 5 ml (1 tsp) margarine and Date and Fig Spread (page 60)

Mid-morning

- 1 serve wholemeal biscuits spread with 5 ml (1 tsp) margarine

Lunch

- 1 sandwich made with 2 slices wholemeal bread spread with 10 ml (2 tsp) peanut butter and filled with chopped celery and lettuce
- 1 sandwich made with 2 slices wholemeal bread, each spread with 5 ml (1 tsp) margarine, and filled with grated carrot, a sprinkling of sultanas and Creamy Yoghurt Dressing (page 158)
- 1 apple
- 2 mandarins

Afternoon Tea

- 2 peaches

Dinner

- Orange Borscht Soup (page 75) prepared with vegetable stock rather than chicken
- 1 wholemeal bread roll with 10 ml (2 tsp) margarine
- 1 serve Jumping Bean Bake (page 119)
- 1 serve Tossed Salad (page 150)
- 1 serve Mocha Mousse (page 179)
- 1 cup canned apricots (no added sugar)

Bedtime Snack

- 2 slices wholemeal bread topped with 45 g (1½ oz) low-fat cheese and grilled

Nutritional Data

Energy & nutrients: 9995 kJ (2388 Cal), 314 g carbohydrate, 116 g protein, 78 g fat
Energy ratio: 51% carbohydrate, 20% protein, 29% fat
Carbohydrate distribution: 79 g breakfast, 13 g mid-morning, 73 g lunch, 14 g afternoon tea, 101 g dinner, 23 g bedtime snack, 12 g from extra milk

TIMING YOUR MEALS

To help you control your blood glucose level, you should eat regular meals.

If you're not on medication, in most cases spreading your carbohydrate evenly between three meals a day is best.

Make sure that you have three to four serves of high-carbohydrate foods per meal, but the punctuality of mealtimes is not as important as it would be if you were on medication, since you will not be prone to low blood glucose (hypoglycaemia). Avoid eating snacks between meals if you are overweight.

If you're on insulin or diabetes tablets

If you are on medication, then you need to ask what type and when to take it. These questions are best answered in conjunction with your dietitian or diabetes specialist. Find out about your medication so that you can design an eating plan that allows your carbohydrate to be spread in such a way as to keep your blood glucose level within normal range.

An even spread of carbohydrate between three meals daily is usually best, although some people find it easier to regulate blood glucose levels if they eat a carbohydrate-rich snack between meals.

You may find that leaving long gaps between meals, or not eating enough carbohydrate at a meal, may cause your blood glucose level to drop too low (we discuss low blood glucose – hypoglycaemia – on page 42). Also important is the need to **keep your carbohydrate intake even from day to day** to prevent unwanted swings in blood glucose level.

Remember, having diabetes does not affect your need for energy, carbohydrate, protein and fat. It only affects the timing and planning of your meals. On the other hand, your meals and meal pattern must suit your lifestyle, and it may be easier to change the timing and dose of your medication rather than your established eating pattern.

Injected insulin and meals

There are various types of insulin available, classified as short, medium, long-acting, or a combination of these depending on when their activity peaks, and the length of action. Short-acting insulins start to lower your blood glucose level immediately after injection; medium and long-acting insulins may take several hours to begin, and then continue to lower your blood glucose level for several more hours.

The time you eat your carbohydrate should match the activity of your insulin. For instance, if you take a short-acting insulin it is important that you have a carbohydrate-rich meal within 30–40 minutes to prevent hypoglycaemia.

If you have a medium or long-acting insulin in the morning, make sure you have a lunch which is rich in carbohydrate. If you have an injection before your evening meal, the carbohydrate content of your meal and/or supper should be high, depending on the type of insulin.

If your mealtime is delayed, you may have to take a small carbohydrate snack to prevent your blood glucose level dropping too low before you have your next meal.

EATING OUT

Having diabetes does not mean you have to miss out on the good things in life, such as eating out. What it does mean is that you need to understand your diabetes and how to manage it so that you live the way you want to. Armed with this book and a bit of practice, you will build up the necessary confidence.

Finding your way round the menu

Meals in restaurants don't have to be dull — only a few simple changes can make most menus fit your needs.

The waiter can tell you what is in the dishes if you are unsure.

Because restaurant foods may be high in kilojoules (calories), you would be wise to limit yourself to a starter and main course, or to a main course and fruit dessert.

SOUPS: Thickened and 'creamed' soups may be high in fats. Ask the waiter to leave out the cream. Or ask for a clear soup or a minestrone.

ENTRÉES (STARTERS): Good choices are vegetable parcels, skewered meats, seafood on rice, salads, asparagus spears, pasta with vegetable sauce, or fresh oysters for a celebration.

MAIN COURSES: Ask for small servings of lean chicken, fish, meat or seafood. Vegetarian and pasta dishes are fine, provided they are not loaded with cream, butter or cheese. To accompany your main course choose pasta, potato or rice to give you plenty of carbohydrate, and other vegetables and salads to add variety, flavour and colour.

BREAD: If the meal you choose does not contain enough carbohydrate, ask for extra bread.

DESSERTS: These are often high in fats, and may contain more sugar than is desirable. If having something sweet to end a meal is important to you, ask for fruit, a simple fruit dessert, a crème caramel or hot soufflé served without cream or rich sauces.

BEVERAGES: Limit your alcohol intake and don't be afraid to ask for a jug of iced water or a glass of soda water.

Ethnic restaurants

Many ethnic restaurants offer good choices. The following ideas may get you started.

Italian: Minestrone soup. Pasta with a seafood or tomato sauce, plain salad, fruit platter.
Chinese: Short soup, combination, seafood or meat and vegetables or whole fish in ginger, steamed vegetables and rice.
Greek: Dolmades, souvlaki, tabbouleh or green salad without dressing, plain pita bread.
Mexican: Taco or burritos. Green salad with salsa, re-fried beans, plain tortillas.
Indian: Tandoori chicken or fish, riata, vegetable curry, chapatis, plain rice.

Take-away meals

These are often high in fat and salt. The following are better choices in terms of fat:

- Sandwiches, rolls or filled pitta bread, hamburger (plain meat and salad), souvlaki, barbecued chicken (don't eat the skin, it's fatty), preferably char-grilled, steamed din sum, hot dog, wholemeal pasty, jacket potatoes.

Where possible, order some fresh salad or fruit to balance the meal.

Treats and special occasions

Christmas, birthdays and other family get-togethers are especially tempting. If you are the host, choose special recipes from this book for just such occasions. If you are a guest, have a little of the dishes you like, but balance this with vegetables, salad, bread and fruit.

A splurge now and then, on special occasions, does no harm; it's what you do for the rest of the time that counts. Return to your usual eating patterns the next day. Frequent splurging will contribute to weight gain and poorly controlled diabetes.

TRAVEL

When travelling short distances, try to have your meals at the normal times. When travelling by car, carry biscuits and fresh or dried fruits, to eat if there are delays.

Overseas travel may mean a change in your normal pattern, particularly when you fly across time zones. It is advisable to notify the airline well in advance and request additional fresh fruit, breads, sandwiches and dry biscuits.

If you are going to cross time zones, discuss your insulin and food requirements with your diabetic team before you leave on the trip.

When travelling in different countries, you can always find suitable food even if it is limited in variety.

SHIFT WORK

If you are a shift worker, the timing of your meals and medications may vary with the timing of your shifts. Because of the great variation in shifts and individual needs, it is difficult to do more than strongly advise you to ask a dietitian or diabetes specialist nurse for suggestions.

Basically you should aim to spread your meals and diabetes medication throughout your waking hours, just as you would on day shift — and treat the day as night. If you take your medication prior to going to bed, make sure that you have also eaten.

SPECIAL NEEDS

HYPOGLYCAEMIA

When your blood glucose level drops too low, this is known as hypoglycaemia, or 'hypo'. Hypoglycaemia is defined as a blood glucose level below 3.5 mmol/litre, and can happen to you if you are on insulin or diabetes tablets. **It does not happen** if you are being treated by diet alone.

How to recognise hypoglycaemia

The symptoms set in quickly. You may experience **one** or **more** of the following:

- Headache
- Dizziness, vagueness
- Extreme hunger
- Blurred vision
- Odd behaviour (such as bad temper, crying)

- Sweating
- Pins and needles around the mouth
- Paleness, trembling, shaking
- Drowsiness

These signs tell you that your blood glucose level may have dropped too low. Some people who test their blood glucose level regularly may find that their level drops too low without experiencing any symptoms. If your blood glucose level drops below 3.5 mmol/l, it should be treated as hypoglycaemia whether you have symptoms or not.

What you should do

Step 1. **Immediately** take sugar to raise your blood glucose level. Any form of sugar will do such as:

- A standard soft drink — one glass
- Sweetened or unsweetened fruit juice — one glass
- Sweets or chocolate — 4 – 5 sweets or squares of chocolate
- Sugar in water — about 15 ml (3 tsp) in 250 ml (8 fl oz, 1 cup) of water
- Honey or jam — about 20 ml (4 tsp).

Do not use low-joule (low-calorie) soft drinks to treat hypoglycaemia.

Step 2. If the symptoms don't improve in 5 minutes, or become worse, take more sugar as above.

Step 3. If still no improvement in 10 minutes, **contact your doctor or local hospital without delay**.

Step 4. Always follow the concentrated sugar with a snack of more complex carbohydrate such as fruit, bread, milk or biscuits, or have your next meal if it is due. This will help to prevent your blood glucose level from falling again.

Do not count any extra food taken to treat hypoglycaemia as part of your regular meal plan. Continue with your usual meals.

If not treated **promptly** and **properly**, hypoglycaemia can worsen and lead to unconsciousness. If this happens, others (family, friends, work mates) need to know what to do:

- Roll the person onto their left side. Make sure the airway is clear by tilting the chin up and check that the tongue hasn't rolled back.

- Call a doctor or ambulance immediately.

- **Never** give an unconscious person anything to eat or drink.

Medical treatment: The doctor will usually give an injection of a hormone called glucagon which stimulates the liver to release glucose into the bloodstream. Alternatively, he or she may inject a special glucose solution directly into the vein. However, be reassured that the person will come out of the coma in 1 – 2 hours but will have a severe headache.

Why it happens

- Taking too much insulin

- A meal delayed too long

- Not enough carbohydrate in your food

- Extra activity (without having extra carbohydrate foods to supply the extra energy — exercise uses your blood glucose supplies)

- Excess alcohol without carbohydrate — such as drinking whisky on an empty stomach

Simple precautions to prevent hypoglycaemia

- Check your food intake to make sure you are having enough carbohydrate with each meal. If meals are delayed, have some carbohydrate in the form of a snack to tide you over.

- Check your dose of insulin or tablets carefully. Taking too much can make your blood glucose level fall too low.

- If you are more active than usual, you may need extra carbohydrate before, during and after the activity (see *Exercise, Sport and Diabetes*, page 51).

- If you are drinking alcohol, make sure you eat food containing carbohydrate with it.

Important: If you are having 'hypos' often, consult your doctor to discuss possible causes and solutions. If your diabetes is well-controlled, you shouldn't have frequent 'hypos'.

WHAT TO DO IF YOU ARE ILL

If your diabetes is controlled without medication, don't worry if you are unable to eat properly for a day or two. Eat and drink as desired. If you are unwell for longer than this, discuss it with your doctor.

If you are on insulin or diabetes tablets, you must continue with your medication as usual, **no matter how awful you are feeling**. One of the side-effects of various illnesses is that your blood glucose level rises, so your medications are absolutely vital to control this. Equally importantly, you must keep on taking carbohydrate even if you are off your food. To do this, try light meals, drinks high in carbohydrates (we've given a number of suitable recipes) or high-carbohydrate snacks. You may find it easier to have a snack or drink every hour, rather than attempt your usual daily meal pattern. **If you are ill for more than two days, or if your blood glucose is consistently higher than 15 mmol/litre, contact your doctor. The following are easy sources of carbohydrate if you are on medication:**

- Homemade or canned soup with toast or dry biscuits
- Standard commercially prepared jelly
- Creamy rice
- Dry biscuits
- Plain sweet biscuit or cake
- Dry biscuits with thinly sliced cheese, tomato or yeast extract
- Ice-cream

- Standard lemonade, ginger ale or other soft drink
- Junket
- Plain boiled rice or pasta (noodles)
- Toast or sandwich
- Stewed or canned fruit
- Milk drinks such as Ovaltine Lite or Low-fat Horlicks
- Fruit juice.

If nauseous or vomiting, try sipping drinks such as: dry ginger ale or lemonade, Lucozade™, Enos™, or dry ginger ale or lemonade with ice cream or milk.

Once you can tolerate any of the above, nibble on a dry biscuit or toast, sip chicken noodle soup or try grated apple mixed with a little orange juice.

> ***Vomiting or diarrhoea***
> *If you are vomiting or suffering from diarrhoea, be aware that it can lead to dehydration and uncontrolled diabetes. You need urgent treatment so contact your doctor right away.*

HIGH BLOOD PRESSURE

Many people with high blood pressure can lower it by limiting the amount of salt (sodium) in their diet. If overweight, try to reduce your weight as another means of controlling your blood pressure.

If you have high blood pressure you would be wise to:

- Limit the amount of salt you use in cooking

- Avoid adding salt at the table

- Limit the amount of highly salted processed food you eat.

A note about salt

We have used a little salt where necessary in our recipes. Some dishes simply taste too bland and unappealing without it. However, we suggest that you always check the flavour of your food before adding salt. Also, remember that in about three weeks you can train your taste-buds to appreciate food with less salt, simply by cutting back on the amount of salt you normally add.

Here is a list of some of the flavouring agents and processed foods which are high in salt:

- Rock, flavoured and vegetable salts — all of them are salt, no matter what the name

- Monosodium glutamate, flavour boosters, meat and vegetable extracts, broth, stock cubes and stock powders, packet soups

- Salted, smoked, cured or pickled meat and fish

- Condiments (sauces), pickles, chutneys, relishes and dressings

- Canned meat, fish and vegetables

- Salted snacks, including potato and corn crisps, nuts and salted biscuits

- Take-away foods such as pizza, barbecued chickens

- Cheese.

Salt substitutes replace all or part of the sodium chloride with potassium chloride. Although these are a satisfactory substitute for ordinary salt, we would prefer you to train your taste-buds to enjoy low-salt foods.

There are many commercial products which are salt-reduced. Use them in place of the standard products and learn to read labels. Look out for the words sodium and salt, and for the food additive number 621 as this stands for monosodium glutamate.

Another way in which to give your food zest without using added salt is through herbs and spices. Try adding lemon juice, tomato, onion, garlic or vinegar for extra flavour.

IF YOU HAVE HIGH BLOOD FAT LEVELS (CHOLESTEROL AND TRIGLYCERIDES)

People who have high blood fat levels have an increased risk of heart and blood vessel disease. You run this risk regardless of whether you are overweight or normal weight. The blood fats of concern are cholesterol and triglycerides. Both of these fats are made in the body as well as being provided in foods.

Dietary fats include cholesterol and triglycerides.

Cholesterol is found only in animal products, while triglycerides are found in both animal and vegetable foods.

Foods high in cholesterol include egg yolk, brains, liver, fatty cuts of meat, prawns, squid, fish roe and dairy foods such as cream, butter and cheese.

Ninety five per cent of fat in the diet is in the form of triglycerides. These fats can be categorised as saturated, monounsaturated or polyunsaturated according to their chemical structure. Animal fats are high in saturated fats which may cause a rise in blood fats and contribute to heart disease. Vegetable fats/oils tend to be higher in monounsaturated and polyunsaturated fats which protect against heart disease.

Fats which are highly saturated include those in meats and dairy foods, and the vegetable fats in cocoa butter and coconut.

Fats which are highly unsaturated (monounsaturated or polyunsaturated) include those in seeds, nuts, olives and avocado or oils made from these foods.

Note: Saturated Vegetable Fats

Be aware that many commercial foods and 'take-aways' contain vegetable fats that have been hydrogenated. This process changes the fats to saturated fats. It is wise to read labels where possible and to limit the use of commercially prepared high fat and fried foods.

Polyunsaturated and monounsaturated oils and margarines are still high in fats, so they should be used sparingly, particularly if you are overweight.

Although an intake of foods high in fat may increase triglyceride levels, this level can also be raised by alcohol and by eating excessive amounts of refined carbohydrate. High triglyceride levels may also be found in overweight people and in people with undiagnosed or poorly controlled diabetes. Weight loss and establishing good control of diabetes will help reduce these levels.

Take very seriously our constant reminder to cut down on all fats. Generally, limit all fats and, in particular, animal fats in your diet. See page 20 for 'Hints to help you use less fat'.

If you are concerned about the amount of fat in your diet or require greater detail on the types of fats, consult a dietitian or contact your regional division of the Heart Foundation of South Africa.

PREGNANCY AND DIABETES

Diabetes should not stand in the way of a normal, healthy pregnancy. If you have diabetes, make sure that it is controlled where possible before you become pregnant. You will find that both your nutritional needs and insulin dosage may need changing while you are pregnant. Get expert help from a dietitian and diabetes specialist and have your diabetes reviewed frequently during pregnancy so your baby gets the best possible start and you maintain your health throughout.

You may also need to change the timing of your carbohydrate intake at this time, to help with management of your diabetes. **It is particularly important that you eat regular meals, especially breakfast and a bedtime snack.** Long periods without food may increase your risk of ketosis which can be harmful to you and to your baby.

Developing diabetes while pregnant (gestational diabetes)

Some women develop diabetes for the first time during pregnancy, usually after the 26th week. Once the baby is born, the symptoms may disappear, and reappear in later pregnancies. About 50 per cent of women with gestational diabetes develop diabetes again in later life.

To ensure that you and your baby are healthy you must take particular care of your diet throughout your pregnancy. This is usually all that is needed to control your blood glucose level.

Furthermore, if you control your weight from then on, and make sure your diet is low in fats and added sugars, while high in complex carbohydrate and fibre, you can help prevent or delay the onset of diabetes in later life. This underscores an important point: **good nutrition and keeping slim are two of your best protections** against developing diabetes.

CHILDREN AND ADOLESCENTS

The guidelines set out in this book will ensure that children and adolescents with diabetes enjoy the benefits of up-to-date dietary management. Just as their insulin requirements will vary, so will their dietary needs; it is strongly recommended that your child or adolescent's diet is reviewed regularly and that their diabetes and general health is monitored regularly. However, do remember that for children and adolescents in particular, food has important social implications. Food and eating should not become a source of family tension. The entire family would benefit by having the same healthy diet, so there is no question of the child or adolescent feeling different.

There is a common misconception that the food you should prepare for diabetics is unpalatable and 'unusual'. The menu plans and recipes in this book show just how wrong this view is; teach your children about a varied, balanced eating plan, encourage them to develop a liking for cereals, vegetables and fruit, and you will have achieved something of lifelong value.

Be flexible and prepare healthy food that delights and satisfies. Remember, too, that children and adolescents like to nibble, so prepare healthy and delicious snacks in advance so that you don't hear the complaint 'There's nothing to eat'. Providing alternatives to fast foods and processed products is half the battle; good sense will see you through the rest.

Tips and traps for children and adolescents

- With young children, it is important that they learn to take an active part in their diabetes management, including blood glucose monitoring, their insulin injections, food choices and planning their meals. You will find that the more involved your child is, the less tension is likely to arise.

- Avoid making diabetes the focus of family life; it's just one aspect. Don't force your child to eat unless he/she has had an insulin injection, in which case food is essential. Forcing a reluctant child to eat leads to resentment, rebellion and anxiety for everyone. It's totally counter-productive. You may find, in the name of co-operation and family well-being, that sometimes you have to make a temporary compromise on diabetes control for the sake of long-term out-come. But balancing the blood glucose lowering effect of insulin with the blood glucose raising effect of food remains pivotal to the control of diabetes.

- By learning to monitor his or her own blood glucose level, your child will soon learn the effects different foods have on it.

- Teach your children the benefits of regular meals and a healthy way of eating. It's an investment in their future health. Use this approach and your child will come to see healthy eating as a positive aspect of life rather than as a negative aspect of having diabetes. Children (and adults for that matter) should learn that diabetes does not mean being punished or deprived of food.

- It's easy for parents to fall into the trap of replacing uneaten vegetables and cereals with sugary foods because you are afraid of your child becoming hypoglycaemic. Children are smart and they will soon learn how to manipulate you; they may start refusing their meals knowing you may offer them a sweet treat instead. Try offering healthier alternatives in this situation: fruit, milk or dry biscuits will do the trick.

- Encourage your child to carry extra snacks, especially when they will be away from home for long periods such as sleeping out at weekends or going to after-school activities.

- Make sure parents of friends, and teachers at school, know that your child has diabetes and that they know how to cope with hypoglycaemia and sickness.

- Let your child know that there are other children with diabetes. They are neither alone nor unique. Diabetes camps are an excellent way to reduce any sense of isolation. For details of these camps, get in touch with your national diabetic association or a local children's hospital.

- Diabetes is not a barrier to normal childhood activities such as parties, sport, staying at friends, trips or school camps, and you should encourage your child to take part.

- The better your child understands his or her diabetes, the more responsibility they will take for it, thus coping better with their own changing needs as they grow older.

Foreground: curry accompaniments – Fresh Mango Chutney, low-fat yoghurt and Riata – beside rough-textured bread. Centre left Vegetable Curry and right, Beef Curry served with steamed brown rice, and Moong Dahl (at the top).

- Don't turn your child into a 'cupboard eater' or 'food sneak' by never letting them taste sweet foods. That old phrase, 'moderation in all things' holds good. You may well find that denying your child any sweet foods leads to secret eating and binges. Simply don't make a fuss about fatty or sweet foods; offer delicious low-fat and low-sugar alternatives. But remember that the occasional splurge will not cause any long-term harm.

- Adolescence brings its own special needs. The teens are a time of exploration, testing and a desire or need for independence. This applies to the issue of food just as much as it does to other realms of behaviour. If your teenager has a good knowledge of diabetes management, they will know how to be flexible in terms of mealtimes, foods eaten, the amount of insulin they need and when they need it. This may cause you considerable anxiety, but you must learn to encourage your child's sense of independence, allow them to learn by their own mistakes.

- For adolescents, the peer pressure to drink alcohol may be strong. Make sure your teenager understands how vital it is to have plenty of carbohydrate when they drink alcohol.

- Adolescents also need to realise **how vital it is to seek medical help the moment they don't feel well.** Failure to do this is a common cause of hospital admissions for uncontrolled diabetes.

- Hormonal changes and growth spurts during adolescence may upset your adolescent's diabetes control even though they are doing the right thing. It may be that their whole management routine needs a fresh appraisal.

VEGETARIANS WITH DIABETES

The guidelines in this book are ideal for people who are vegetarian. Many of the recipes have been created with vegetarians in mind, and on page 36 you will find vegetarian meal plans showing how to balance your nutritional needs.

You can follow a vegetarian diet, be well nourished and keep your diabetes under control. But you should be aware that as a vegetarian you can miss out on some nutrients. It is therefore vital that you know how to plan your diet to ensure these are included in adequate amounts.

To begin with, we suggest that you include dairy products and eggs in your vegetarian eating plan (in other words, what is termed 'lacto-ovo vegetarian'). However, if you choose to follow a strict vegan lifestyle (in other words, do not eat any animal products at all), we strongly recommend that you consult a dietitian, who will help you to plan an adequate diet.

Tips and traps for vegetarians

- The nutrients you may be lacking in a poorly planned diet are: iron, zinc, protein, calcium, cyanocobalamin (Vitamin B12) and riboflavin (B2).

Toast and Stawberry Conserve, a bowl of Meg's Muesli with a lavish sprinkling of cashew nuts, Fruit Compote and, at the back, a refreshing glass of Orange Buttermilk.

- The best sources of iron and zinc for vegetarians are pulses, wholegrain cereal products, green leafy vegetables and eggs. However, these foods do not release their minerals into your system as readily as animal sources do, such as meat.

- To increase your absorption of iron from non-meat sources, include foods with Vitamin C at the same meal. For instance, include citrus fruits, pineapple, tomatoes or juice made from them when you eat iron-rich food such as cereal products, spinach or Swiss chard (silverbeet).

- The tannin in tea interferes with the absorption of iron into your body, so don't finish your meal with a cup of tea.

- Fibre slows the absorption of vitamins and minerals in your digestive tract, so you may have to eat more of certain foods to counter this.

- Eat the recommended daily amounts of dairy products and eggs set out below, to ensure your protein, calcium, cyanocobalamin (B12) and riboflavin (B2) needs are met.

A Guide to Recommended Daily Food Intake for Lacto-Ovo Vegetarians

Milk and dairy products

600 ml (1 pint, 2 1/2 cups) milk or the equivalent in cheese and/or yoghurt

250 ml (8 fl oz, 1 cup) milk = 30 g (1 oz) hard cheese

or   = 250 ml (8 fl oz, 1 cup) yoghurt

Note: Low-fat cheeses such as cottage and ricotta are poor sources of calcium.

Other protein-rich foods

We recommend that you eat two serves of the following every day:

- eggs   1 serve = 2
- pulses   1 serve = 150 g (5 oz, 3/4 cup) cooked
- nuts   1 serve = 90 g (3 oz, 3/4 cup)
- soy bean curd (tofu)   1 serve = 225 g (7 1/2 oz, 1 cup)

Note: Because vegetarian diets are generally low in high-cholesterol foods, don't worry about limiting your intake of eggs.

Guidelines for other foods

Make sure that your daily diet also includes:

Fruits and vegetables   at least 4 – 5 serves

Bread and cereals   a minimum of 4 serves or more, according to appetite

Fats   15 – 30 g (1/2 – 1 oz) including some table margarine

Tips for vegans

- Suitable protein sources include soya milk, pulses, nuts, seeds and cereal products. As the protein quality from these sources is not as good as animal sources, you need to eat a variety of these products every day.

- Alternative cyanocobalamin (B12) sources include fortified soya milk (check the label). As only a few milks are fortified, a supplement is recommended.

- Alternative calcium sources include fortified soya milk (check the label), sesame seeds, tahini and almonds.

- Alternative riboflavin (B2) sources include fortified soya milk (check the label), yeast extract, dried fruits, pulses, nuts and green leafy vegetables.

A note about soya milk and diabetes

Many brands of soya milk have added sugar (usually in the form of sucrose).
This is also common in flavoured soya milk, so we advise you to read the labels carefully.

EXERCISE, SPORT AND DIABETES

Regular exercise is important for everyone who wants to achieve and maintain good health. 'Regular exercise' means at least 30 minutes of, say, brisk walking, swimming, bicycling or aerobics, three times a week. To know whether your body is benefiting from exercise, check your pulse immediately afterwards; it should be faster than your usual resting level.

For people with diabetes, exercise has another function — it helps to keep their blood glucose level within normal range. People with **non-insulin dependent diabetes** can improve their diabetes control and minimize their need for medication by exercising or playing sport regularly.

If you have insulin-dependent diabetes, regular exercise is important, but requires more careful planning. You will learn from experience how your body reacts to exercise and how best to balance your energy expenditure with the needs of your diabetes.

EXERCISE AND YOUR BLOOD GLUCOSE LEVEL

For the person without diabetes

The body is able to keep blood glucose level constant during sport through the release of insulin and other hormones.
***When exercise begins**, the body normally stops releasing insulin and produces the hormones adrenalin and glucagon which stimulate the liver to release glucose into the blood. The insulin already present in the bloodstream allows the exercising muscles to take up the glucose, converting it to energy and keeping the blood glucose level constant.*

As the exercise continues, the blood glucose level normally goes up slightly and the liver then stops releasing glucose. Now the body releases insulin again, so that more glucose can pass into the exercising muscle. This complex mechanism ensures that the blood glucose level normally remains constant.

What happens if you have insulin-dependent diabetes?

*If you have insulin-dependent diabetes, you don't have the benefit of this natural control. Once you have taken your insulin injection, you cannot regulate its action. This means that you may have a wide variation in your blood glucose level during and after exercise. However, **if you have enough insulin** in your system and your blood glucose level is within the normal range at the start of exercise, then you can safely exercise.*

***If you don't have enough insulin** available in your system when you begin exercising — in other words, your blood glucose level is high — your body can misread the situation and release more glucose into your bloodstream from the liver. Because you don't have enough insulin, the glucose can't pass into your muscle cells. As a result, your blood glucose level will rise excessively (hyperglycaemia). So check your glucose levels before you begin. You shouldn't exercise if your blood glucose is above 16 mmol/l.*

***If, on the other hand you have too much insulin** in your blood and your blood glucose level is low, your liver shuts down its release of glucose. The insulin continues to carry glucose to your muscles, leading to a rapid fall in your blood glucose level (hypoglycaemia).*

Tips and traps when exercising

Hypoglycaemia is the most common concern for people on diabetes medication who exercise regularly. However, there are some simple steps you can take to help to prevent this problem.

- Where possible, check your blood glucose level before you exercise, especially if you are new to diabetes. If you feel your level is low, then take a carbohydrate snack before you begin exercising. You may find it useful to take another test after the exercise or during it if it is prolonged, so you become familiar with the effect exercise has on your levels.

- If you are exercising away from home, make sure you have some carbohydrate foods with you, such as fruit, fruit juice, barley sugar or biscuits.

- If you have been doing vigorous exercise, your blood glucose level may continue to drop after you stop exercising for up to half an hour, so you should eat some carbohydrate afterwards, too.

- Be aware of dehydration. But don't confuse this with hypoglycaemia which relates not to fluids but to blood glucose level. If you exercise vigorously in hot weather, keep drinking plenty of fluids before, during and after your exercise.

- You may wish to reduce your insulin prior to exercise so that you do not need to eat as much carbohydrate.

- When your exercise session is over, quench your thirst with a non-alcoholic drink. Alcohol may lower your blood glucose level further and also has a dehydrating effect.

- Serious athletes with diabetes (and there are plenty of them), ensure that their diabetes is well controlled before they begin training. Training is the time to fine-tune control. They know that this will ensure peak performance during competition.

Don't forget your fluids!

How to adjust your food intake

Once your diabetes is controlled, you will need to learn how to manipulate the balance between food, insulin and activity. The only way to do this properly is to monitor your blood glucose level before, during and after your exercise and experiment until you are confident about the combination which suits your needs best.

It may help to use this ready-reckoner as a starting point to work out your carbohydrate intake and adjust it to suit your individual needs, but discuss these first with your diabetic team.

Activity	Time	Blood Glucose Level MMOL/L prior to activity	Recommended additional carbohydrate intake
Low level	1/2 hour	<5.5	10 g CHO (small serve fruit, bread, biscuit, yoghurt or milk)
		>5.6	No extra food
Moderate intensity	1 hour	<5.5	20 – 30 g CHO (1 1/2 – 2 serves fruit, bread, biscuits, yoghurt and/or milk)
		5.6 – 10	10 g CHO (small serve fruit, bread, biscuit, yoghurt or milk)
		10 – 16	No extra food (in most cases)
		>16	No extra food. Exercise not recommended, blood glucose level may go up
Strenuous activity	1 – 2 hours	<5.5	45 – 60 g CHO (1 sandwich and fruit and/or milk or yoghurt)
		5.6 – 10	25 – 50 g CHO (1 sandwich and fruit and/or milk or yoghurt)
		10 – 16	15 g CHO (1 serve fruit, bread, biscuits, yoghurt or milk)
		>16	Exercise not recommended, blood glucose level may go up
Varying intensity	Long		Insulin may best be decreased. (Conservatively decrease the insulin dose due to peak at time of activity by 10 per cent.)
	Duration 1/2 – 1 day		(A 50 per cent reduction is not uncommon.) Increase CHO before, during and after activity 10 – 50 g CHO per hour, such as diluted fruit juice

CHO = Carbohydrate

HOW TO MODIFY RECIPES

Some of your old family favourite recipes may seem unsuitable if you have diabetes. Before putting them away, see if you can alter them to suit your new eating pattern. You may be able to reduce the fat and sugar, and increase the fibre without changing the flavour or appearance of the dish very much, if at all.

We have taken a typical family dish to show you how to adapt it. *The changes in ingredients and method are shown in italics.*

Bread and Butter Pudding

4 thin slices bread	*Use wholemeal bread*
90 g (3 oz) sugar	*Use an artifical sweetener or 20 ml (4 tsp) sugar and vanilla essence for more flavour*
90 g (3 oz, ¹/₂ cup) raisins	
30 g (1 oz) butter	*Use margarine — 15 ml (3 tsp) should be enough*
2 eggs	
600 ml (1 pint, 2¹/₂ cups) milk	*Use low-fat milk*

1.   Grease a pie dish.

     No need to grease.

2.   Spread the bread with butter (*margarine*) and layer it in the dish with sugar and raisins sprinkled in between.

     Use far less sugar or if you prefer a sweet pudding, add sweetener to the eggs and milk.

3.   Beat the eggs and milk.

     Add sweetener and vanilla essence if preferred to sugar.

4.   Pour egg mixture over the bread and leave to stand for 10 minutes. Then bake in moderate oven until the custard is set, about 20 – 25 minutes.

Tips and traps in modifying recipes

MAIN DISHES

●   Consider whether you can cut down on the amount of meat. 125 g (4 oz) per person is sufficient. This means 500 g (1 lb) should feed four.

●   Choose lean cuts and trim off any visible fat.

●   If bacon is used as a flavouring, try using a little very lean ham, ham bone or bacon stock cube instead — in which case you will not need to add more salt.

- Reduce fats. For browning foods, use a non-stick pan over high heat to dry-fry foods such as meat. Alternatively, use a pastry brush to brush a thin layer of oil on the base of the pan — you really need very little to do the trick — or try adding lemon juice.

- Don't use more than 10 ml (2 tsp) of added fat for a recipe serving four or leave out the fat if you can.

- If a recipe uses any form of cream as a sauce, you can often use low-fat yoghurt instead, but remember to add it at the last minute and not allow the sauce to reboil or the yoghurt will curdle.

- For white sauces, use low-fat or skim milk in place of full-cream milk. Use the minimum amount of butter or margarine, or use cornflour (cornstarch) with low-fat milk and don't use any fat.

- To add fibre and decrease the meat, include some dried beans or lentils in mixed dishes with meat. This works wonderfully in pasta sauces, lasagne, curries and casseroles.

- If a dish calls for pasta or rice, use brown rice and wholemeal pasta rather than the refined varieties. If you don't like this, try mixing the refined and unrefined types half and half, but watch the cooking times as these may be different.

DESSERTS AND CAKES

Many of these recipes modify well, so try your old standbys with a few changes, such as:

- Substitute wholemeal flour for white, or, if the result is too heavy, use a half-and-half mixture.

- If you substitute wholemeal flour in a recipe, you usually have to add a little more liquid to get a moist result.

- Substitute skimmed or low-fat milk for full-cream milk.

- Cut down on or omit the butter or margarine. Where a recipe specifies that you cream butter and sugar, minimize the sugar, reduce the butter and rub into the dry ingredients.

- Where you have cut down on butter and sugar in a recipe, the result will not rise as high, and the texture will be a little denser than the unmodified version. Try using a smaller baking tin if necessary.

And if your recipe can't be modified ...

Some recipes simply don't look and taste the same if modified. Put these on your list of occasional dishes and keep them as treats — and then only have a small serving.

PLEASURES OF THE TABLE

Using the recipes in this book

Most of the recipes in this book are simple and quick to prepare. In most cases, we avoid using unusual ingredients, although we slip some in now and again to encourage you to experiment.

Flavour: You can increase or decrease the flavour intensity of recipes to suit your own taste. Experiment with herbs and spices; cut back or add more as you like. Such flavour enhancers will not alter the nutritional value of your food.

If microwaving any of the dishes, you may need to increase the amount of herbs and spices we recommend because microwaving does not always allow for the flavours to develop and combine.

Salt: We follow the good health guideline of 'cut back on salt'. However, we use common sense, and, where we feel that a recipe needs a little salt, we add soy sauce or stock cubes.

We encourage you to minimize or omit salt wherever possible. Where we refer to soy sauce in the recipes, we suggest you use light or salt-reduced soy sauce.

Sugar: We use a variety of sweetening agents in our recipes, including sugar in small amounts. There are good reasons for this. Firstly, we now know that a small amount of sugar taken in a mixed meal or recipe does not cause a significant rise in blood glucose level. Secondly, some recipes, especially for baked products, rely on sugar to produce good results. Thirdly, there are some instances where the flavour of sugar is superior to that of artificial sweeteners — it does not alter or lose taste during the cooking process.

You will also see that we use natural sweetening agents other than sugar, such as fruit juice, dried fruits and fruit juice concentrates, with delicious results.

Fat: We use a number of ways to reduce the fat content of our recipes. For example, we frequently sauté using water or a hot dry pan instead of oil. Where oil is used we have kept it to a minimum by recommending that you brush the frying pan with oil rather than pouring it in.

Generally we use skimmed or low-fat milk ($1\frac{1}{2}$ – 2 per cent fat). Likewise, with yoghurt; in most cases, you can substitute low-fat plain yoghurt for full-cream yoghurt. But not always: for instance, full-cream yoghurt is absolutely necessary in Quick Wholemeal Bread (page 187).

Where we use cottage cheese, it is always the skimmed milk variety; ricotta cheese is always smooth ricotta (9 – 11 per cent fat); low-fat hard cheese is cheese of less than 20 per cent fat. Low-fat soft cheese is a mixture of about half and half curd and cream cheese where you mix your own, or the commercial variety of about 14 per cent fat. To enhance the flavour of some recipes, we include a small amount of higher-fat tasty cheeses, such as Parmesan. Here, we use the principle that a small amount goes a long way.

Fibre: We use wholemeal products as much as possible. However, there are times when the texture or flavour of the dish is better with a mixture of wholegrain and refined flours or cereals. In a few recipes, we use the refined product only to give a more traditional result. Using wholemeal flour products gives a heavier or denser texture than white flour, and requires more liquid during cooking. We allow for this is our recipes.

When using the oven: Always turn your oven on in plenty of time so it is at the correct temperature when you are ready to use it.

Analysis: Where a choice of ingredients is given in a recipe, the first one listed is the one we use in our analysis of nutritional value.

HAPPY COOKING!

Breakfasts

For a good start to a great day, make sure you have breakfast. We've given ideas from leisurely Sunday breakfasts through to simple quick ideas for the weekday rush. Breakfasts can be as simple as a bowl of cereal and a portion of fruit, or as beguiling as a fruit platter followed by mouthwatering pancakes.

Breakfast is the ideal meal in which to boost your carbohydrate and fibre intake. Begin with a breakfast cereal. These can be home-made or you can choose from the excellent commercial products available. Look at our list on page 38 to see the ones we recommend. Porridge (cooked cereal) makes a terrific start to the day and lends itself to interesting toppings such as nuts, sultanas, diced raw apple and cinnamon.

As the following recipe shows, you can combine various grains, either cooked or raw, to make your personal breakfast blend. In addition to the ingredients in Meg's Muesli, consider these:

oats; All Bran; wheatgerm; bran (all sorts — rice, corn, oat or wheat); dried fruits of every kind; unsalted raw nuts; seeds (pumpkin, sesame, linseed and sunflower); shredded coconut; millet; puffed rice, wheat or corn; and wheatflakes.

Keep your favourite blend in an airtight container and serve it with hot or cold skimmed milk or low-fat milk or yoghurt.

Meg's Muesli

Makes about
1 kg (2 lb)

---

375 g (12 oz, 4 cups)
* rolled oats*
100 g (3 ½ oz, 2 cups)
* shredded coconut*
170 g (6 oz, 1 cup)
* sultanas*
125 g (4 oz, 1 cup)
* unsalted cashew nuts,*
* chopped*
125 g (4 oz, 2 cups)
* unprocessed bran*
125 g (4 oz, 2 cups)
* All Bran*
90 g (3 oz, 1 ½ cups)
* wheatgerm*

You can develop your own muesli recipe according to taste but be very careful about the ingredients you add — check them against the ready reckoner at the end of this book to find out whether the additional ingredients you want to use have more fat than we recommend. Watch out, too, for added sugar.

Method:

Mix all ingredients well with a large spoon or your fingers. Allow 45 g (1 1/2 oz, 1/3 cup) per serve.

Nutritional data per serve: 470 kJ (112 cal), CHO 12 g, Protein 4 g, Fat 6 g.

Preparation time: 15 minutes.

For your toast or bread, look at the toppings and fillings we've suggested on page 63. Before you reach for the butter or margarine, consider the recipes for Date and Fig Spread, Strawberry Spread, and Dried Apricot Conserve in this section.

Fruit cleanses the palate after the night and provides many vitamins and minerals, as well as carbohydrate and fibre. Eat it fresh, stewed or canned without added sugar. Combine fruits, top them with low-fat yoghurt, cottage cheese, spoon them on to your porridge or cereal, or simply eat them on their own.

Cooked breakfasts are worth waking up early for and they need not take long to prepare.
Try:

- Eggs, poached, scrambled or boiled
- Omelettes with fillings such as low-fat cheese and herbs, tomato combined with lean ham and onion, or a mushroom sauce
- Baked beans with freshly chopped mushrooms or green pepper (capsicum)
- Bubble and squeak
- Sweetcorn mixed with Cheese Sauce (page 152) and finely chopped lean ham.

And if you simply don't have a moment in the morning, our Liquid Breakfast comes in a glass.

Liquid Breakfast

Serves 4

450 ml (¾ pint, 2 cups)
   skimmed or low-fat
   milk
250 ml (8 fl oz, 1 cup)
   low-fat plain yoghurt
3 ripe bananas or 150 g
   (5 oz, 1 cup) fresh
   strawberries or
   unsweetened canned
   peaches or apricots
2 eggs (optional)
artificial sweetener, to
   taste
garnish: ground allspice,
   cinnamon or grated
   nutmeg

This is great for a person 'on the run'. It takes so little time to prepare, tastes great and will get you off to a good start.

Method:

1. Place all ingredients in a blender or food processor and blend well.
2. Serve at once, topped with a sprinkling of spice.

Nutritional data per serve: 749 kJ (179 cal), CHO 26 g, Protein 12 g, Fat 4 g.

Preparation time: 5 minutes. Equipment: food processor or blender.

Coddled Egg

Serves 1

1 egg
1 slice wholemeal bread
2.5 ml (½ tsp) margarine
pepper
pinch of salt

Method:

1. Bring water to boil in saucepan, lower egg in gently and soft boil to taste (3 – 5 minutes).
2. Crumble bread into an individual serving bowl.
3. Add margarine, pepper and salt.
4. Life egg out of water, crack open top and spoon soft egg on to bread mixture.
5. Stir together gently and serve.

To vary: add 2 1/2 ml (1/2 tsp) of finely snipped chives or chopped parsley at step 3.

Nutritional data per serve: 607 kJ (145 cal), CHO 10 g, Protein 8 g, Fat 8 g.

Preparation time: 10 minutes. Cooking equipment: small saucepan.

Fresh Strawberry Conserve

Makes about 250 g
(8 oz, 1 cup)

---

250 g (8 oz) strawberries,
  hulled and roughly
  chopped
20 ml (4 tsp) water
20 ml (4 tsp) lemon juice
5 ml (1 tsp) gelatine
  soaked in 30 ml (6 tsp)
  water
artificial sweetener
  equivalent to 20 ml
  (4 tsp) sugar

You can vary this recipe by using other berries instead of strawberries.

Method:
1. Place strawberries in saucepan with water and lemon juice.
2. Cover, bring to boil and simmer for 10 minutes, or microwave on High for 5 minutes.
3. Mash fruit slightly and leave to stand for 10 minutes.
4. Dissolve gelatine according to instructions on packet and add to fruit.
5. Stir in sweetener.
6. Pour into a clean, hot jar. Cover, cool and refrigerate.

To store: refrigerate for up to two weeks.

Nutritional data per serve: 168 kJ (40 cal), CHO 6 g, Protein 4 g, Fat trace.

Preparation time: 30 minutes. Cooking equipment: small saucepan.

Date and Fig Spread

Makes about 330 g
(11 oz, 2 cups)

---

150 g (5 oz, 1 cup) pitted
  dates
170 g (6 oz, 1 cup) dried
  figs
30 ml (6 tsp) lemon juice
45 ml (9 tsp) orange juice

The dates and figs have all the sweetness you need as a substitute for traditional sugar-laden jams.

Method:
1. Chop fruit finely.
2. Place in bowl, pour juice over, cover and soak overnight.
3. Spoon into blender or food processor and blend for about 2 minutes until smooth.
4. Spoon into a jar and cover.

To store: refrigerate for up to two weeks.

Nutritional data per serve: 3312 kJ (791 cal), CHO 196 g, Protein 10 g, Fat trace.

Preparation time: 15 minutes plus overnight soaking. Cooking equipment: food processor or blender.

Dried Apricot Conserve

Makes about 125 g
(4 oz, 1 cup)

125 g (4 oz, 1 cup)
  dried apricots
juice of 1 orange
pinch of ground
  cinnamon
pinch of ground cloves
125 ml (4 fl oz, ½ cup)
  warm water

You can vary this delectable yet simple recipe by using a dried fruit medley, dried peaches or dried pears. You can also replace the cloves with fresh or ground ginger.

Method:

1. Chop apricots roughly.
2. Combine in mixing bowl with juice, spices and water. Cover. Allow to stand for 1 hour.
3. Spoon into saucepan and cook gently for about 10 minutes over low heat, stirring constantly, until mixture thickens and starts to combine. Alternatively, spoon into a bowl and microwave on High for 5 minutes. Stir two or three times during cooking until mixture thickens and starts to combine.
4. Spoon into container, cover and cool.
5. Stir again, adding a little more water if necessary, then refrigerate until ready to use.

To store: cover and refrigerate for up to two weeks.

Nutritional data per total quantity: 1248 kJ (298 cal), CHO 69 g, Protein 8 g, Fat trace.

Preparation time: 1½ hours. Cooking equipment: small saucepan or microwave dish.

Appetizers and snacks

Here we give you some ideas for quick and light meals, cocktail parties and hors d'oeuvres. Remember the basic principles of low-fat eating when planning appetizers and snacks. The recipes in this section are also a useful source of carbohydrate which you can use to balance your daily meal plan.

If you are overweight, be careful not to over-indulge in these tempters.

Bread, pumpernickel or wholemeal biscuits make a good base for appetizers. Here are a few ideas:

Accompaniments for dips

Vegetables: carrot sticks, cauliflower and broccoli florets, celery sticks, cucumber wedges, green or red pepper (capsicum) pieces, mushrooms (button or sliced), radish wedges, spring onions (shallots).

Fruits: apple wedges tossed in lemon juice to prevent browning, cantaloup (rock melon) or honeydew melon cut into chunks, kiwi fruit wedges, fresh pineapple pieces, pear slices, fresh apricot halves.

Bread and biscuits: crusty wholemeal bread, dark rye or pumpernickel slices, triangles of toast, pitta bread triangles (fresh or toasted), plain dry biscuits, crispbread or rusks.

Asparagus rolls

To serve four, you will need three slices of wholemeal bread and three slices of white high-fibre bread. Cut off the crusts, roll the bread to flatten it a little, spread very lightly with margarine and place a spear of cooked fresh asparagus or canned asparagus diagonally across each slice of bread. Roll the bread towards a corner and press lightly to seal the edges. Cut each in half. Finally, garnish with rings of green or red pepper (capsicum) and parsley.

Pumpernickel savouries

Many different combinations can be used to top rounds or squares of pumpernickel to make interesting and tasty savouries. Try these ideas:

- Prawns or shrimps and avocado
- Smoked salmon slices or rolls garnished with capers
- Sliced hard-boiled egg topped with black caviar and tiny sprigs of parsley
- Circles or squares of lean ham with asparagus tips
- Low-fat cottage cheese topped with strawberry halves or slices of peach or nectarine.

Sandwich fillings

Remember, when you use any of these delicious fillings you do not need to use margarine on the bread — and use wholemeal bread rather than white. Try these fillings on open sandwiches.

Cheese and ...

- A mixture of grated low-fat hard cheese, grated apple, carrot, chopped celery and pecans or walnuts; bind with Creamy Yoghurt Dressing (page 158)
- Ricotta cheese with sliced cucumber, tomato and chopped basil
- Ricotta cheese with chopped celery and walnuts
- Mustard, grated low-fat hard cheese and sliced olives
- Sliced low-fat hard cheese, thinly-sliced green apple and fresh Mango Pickle (page 161)

Fish and ...

- Salmon or tuna in brine, with sliced cucumber or celery, topped with Creamy Yoghurt Dressing (page 158)
- Shrimps, ricotta cheese and thinly sliced cucumber
- Smoked salmon, low-fat soft cheese and capers

Meat or chicken and ...

- Mango Pickle (page 160) or mustard topped with thinly sliced cold lean meat
- Chopped chicken, snipped chives and parsley bound with Creamy Yoghurt Dressing (page 158)
- Chopped chicken, walnuts and celery or green pepper (capsicum), bound with low-fat plain yoghurt
- Whole-seed mustard, chopped lean ham and grated apple
- Chopped chicken topped with thinly sliced raw mushrooms and Curry Dressing (page 160)

Egg and ...

- Scrambled eggs with finely chopped lean ham
- Hard-boiled eggs mashed with alfalfa or bean sprouts (beanshoots) and Curry Dressing (page 160)

Vegetables and ...

- Canned baked beans, lightly mashed and seasoned with Tabasco
- Peanut butter and sliced cucumber or chopped celery
- Mashed kidney beans with chilli, green pepper (capsicum), cucumber and onion

Sweet fillings and ...

- Mashed banana with lemon juice and cinnamon
- Cottage or ricotta cheese with chopped dried figs

Kidney Bean Dip

Makes about 750 g
(1½ lb, 2 cups)

750 g (1 ½ lb) canned red
 kidney beans
1 large onion or 6 – 8
 spring onions (shallots)
salt and pepper
1 firm tomato

Method:

1. Wash and drain kidney beans. Blend in food processor or blender until smooth.
2. Chop onion or spring onions (shallots) finely.
3. Stir seasoning and onion into bean mixture.
4. Chop tomato finely and add.
5. Serve dip in a bowl with accompaniments (page 62).

To store: cover and refrigerate for up to two days.

Nutritional data per total quantity: 3575 kJ (854 cal), CHO 109 g, Protein 93 g, Fat 3 g.

Preparation time: 30 minutes. Cooking equipment: food processor or blender.

Chicken Liver Pâté

Serves 6 as an
appetizer

250 g (8 oz) chicken
 livers
60 ml (2 fl oz, ¼ cup)
 water
1 sprig fresh or a good
 pinch of dried thyme
2 bay leaves
salt and pepper to taste
125 ml (4 fl oz, ½ cup)
 port
garnish: coarsely ground
 black pepper

Chicken liver pâté is usually made with lashings of butter and cream. This recipe avoids additional fats, yet tastes delicious.

Method:

1. Wash, dry and roughly chop the livers, discarding any greenish portions (these are not a sign of deterioration but may discolour the pâté).
2. In a saucepan, bring water to the boil. Add the liver and stir until sealed, about 2 minutes.
3. Add the thyme, bay leaves, salt and pepper. Cover, reduce heat and simmer gently for 10 minutes.
4. Add port and simmer, uncovered, for a further 3 minutes.
5. If using fresh thyme, remove and discard the sprig. Remove and discard bay leaves.
6. Allow mixture to cool slightly. Purée liver and cooking liquids in a food processor or blender.

To vary: replace port with 75 ml (2½ fl oz) each of orange juice and brandy and add the grated rind of half an orange.

To store: cover and refrigerate for up to three days.

To serve as an appetizer: spoon the pâté into a serving bowl, sprinkle with black pepper and chill for at least 1 hour before serving. Surround the dip with sliced fresh vegetables, biscuits or triangles of dry toast.

To serve as an entrée: spoon the pâté into small, individual pots or ramekins. Smooth over the surface, sprinkle with black pepper and chill for at least 1 hour before serving. Place the pots on small plates and arrange a couple of dry toast triangles or crisp biscuits on each plate.

Nutritional data per serve (6 serves as appetizer): 410.2 kJ (98 cal), CHO 3 g, Protein 9 g, Fat 3 g.

Preparation time: 30 minutes. Cooking equipment: heavy-based saucepan, food processor or blender.

Moong Dhal

Makes about 400 g
(14 oz, 2 cups)

200 g (7 oz, 1 cup) dried
  red lentils
750 ml (1¼ pints,
  3 cups) water
2.5 ml (½ tsp) ground
  turmeric
1 tomato, peeled and
  chopped
10 ml (2 tsp) oil
2.5 ml (½ tsp) cumin
  seeds
3 curry leaves (optional)
1 onion, finely chopped
  or minced
2 garlic cloves, finely
  chopped or minced
20 ml (4 tsp) fresh
  ginger, chopped or
  finely minced
30 ml (6 tsp) Curry
  Powder (page 162), or
  to taste
125 ml (4 fl oz, ½ cup)
  boiling water
  (optional)
salt (optional)
garnish: 20 ml (4 tsp)
  chopped fresh
  coriander (optional)

You can also serve this dip as a soup if you dilute it with 450 ml (3/4 pint, 2 cups) of chicken stock.

Method:
1. Wash lentils thoroughly, removing those that float.
2. Add 750 ml (1 1/4 pints, 3 cups) of water, turmeric and chopped tomato, and boil for 20 – 30 minutes until the lentils are soft and the consistency thick.
3. Heat oil in frying pan, add cumin seeds, curry leaves, onion, garlic and ginger and sauté until golden. Stir in curry powder and sauté for 3 – 4 minutes more. If mixture is too thick, add about 125 ml (4 fl oz, 1/2 cup) boiling water. Add this to the cooked lentils and stir well. Add salt if desired.
4. Just before serving garnish with chopped coriander, if using. Serve hot as a dip with accompaniments (page 62).

Microwave: cook lentils on High for 20 minutes, otherwise follow the conventional recipe.

To store: cover and refrigerate for up to two days. Reheat before serving.

Nutritional data per total quantity: 2728 kJ (652 cal), CHO 40 g, Protein 17 g, Fat 47 g.

Preparation time: 1 hour. Cooking equipment: saucepan, frying pan.

Dolmades

Serves 4 – 6

450 ml (¾ pint, 2 cups)
  chicken stock
200 g (7 oz, 1 cup) brown
  rice
1 chicken breast, skinned
  and minced or finely
  chopped
1 pkt preserved vine
  leaves
2.5 ml (½ tsp) cardamon
  seeds, crushed
2.5 ml (½ tsp) salt or
  1 chicken stock cube
10 ml (2 tsp) olive oil
  and 10 ml (2 tsp) extra
1 lemon and juice of
  ½ lemon extra
½ small onion, freshly
  chopped
garnish: chopped parsley

Method:

1. Bring chicken stock to the boil, reduce heat and simmer.
2. Wash rice and add to the stock.
3. Add chicken. Simmer gently, covered, until liquid is absorbed and rice is tender. Add a little water if necessary. Remove from heat.
4. Rinse vine leaves carefully to remove preserving liquid. Drain.
5. To rice mixture, add flavourings, 10 ml (2 tsp) oil, grated rind and juice of 1 lemon, onion and parsley.
6. Place about 20 ml (4 tsp) of mixture on each vine leaf. Wrap firmly into parcels and place in a baking dish. Continue until all the vine leaves are used. Make sure dolmades are firmly packed into dish.
7. Pour a little water into the baking dish until it reaches about 1 cm (1/2 inch) up the side of the dish, squeeze juice of 1/2 lemon over, and sprinkle extra 10 ml (2 tsp) olive oil over.
8. Cover with foil and bake in a preheated oven for about 1 hour.
9. Cool. Serve garnished with parsley.

Accompaniment: Cucumber and Yoghurt Sauce (page 156).

To store: cover and refrigerate for up to three days. Do not store in an aluminium container.

Nutritional data per serve (for 4 serves): 634 kJ (151 cal), CHO 15 g, Protein 9 g, Fat 6 g.

Preparation time: 2 hours. Cooking equipment: saucepan, baking dish.

Oven temperature: 160 °C (325 °F, gas 3).

Chick-Pea Savoury

Makes about 625 g
(1 ¼ lb, 3 cups)

200 g (7 oz, 1 cup) dried
   chick-peas
water
10 ml (2 tsp) oil
2 large onions, chopped
10 ml (2 tsp) crushed
   garlic
10 ml (2 tsp) minced
   fresh ginger
2.5 ml (½ tsp) ground
   turmeric
5 ml (½ tsp) garam
   masala
2 large ripe tomatoes,
   chopped
2 bay leaves
40 ml (8 tsp) fresh
   coriander or mint,
   chopped
lemon juice to taste
salt to taste (optional)

Great served with chappati or pitta bread.

Method:
1. Cover the chick-peas with water and soak overnight.
2. In a saucepan, heat oil and sauté onion, garlic and ginger until golden, stirring frequently. Add turmeric, garam masala, tomatoes, bay leaves and half the fresh herbs. Add chick-peas and soaking liquid, cover and simmer on low heat until peas are tender. Set aside 20 ml (4 tsp) of cooked chick-peas to garnish.
3. Remove bay leaves. Blend cooked chick-peas in food processor or blender until smooth. Add lemon juice and salt if desired.
4. Sprinkle with remaining fresh herbs and the reserved chick-peas.

Nutritional data per portion: 3158 kJ (755 cal), CHO 72 g, Protein 28 g, Fat 39 g.

Preparation time: 1 ½ hours plus overnight soaking.
Cooking equipment: saucepan, food processor or blender.

Cheese Puffs

Serves 4

2 eggs
2 thin slices lean ham,
   chopped
90 g (3 oz) low-fat hard
   cheese, grated
1 small, firm tomato,
   finely chopped
2.5 ml (½ tsp) snipped
   chives
freshly ground black
   pepper
4 slices of wholemeal
   bread

Method:
1. Preheat grill.
2. Place eggs in bowl and beat lightly with a fork.
3. Add remaining ingredients, except bread, and mix.
4. Toast bread on one side, remove from the grill and spread the cheese mixture over the untoasted side of the bread.
5. Grill until the mixture puffs up and browns. Serve hot.

Nutritional data per puff: 784 kJ (187 cal), CHO 10 g, Protein 14 g, Fat 10 g.

Preparation time: 15 minutes.

Vegetable Samosas

Serves 4 – 8
1 – 2 per serve

2 medium potatoes,
  scrubbed and diced

1 medium carrot,
  scrubbed and diced

½ medium sweet potato
  (yam), peeled and
  diced

150 g (5 oz, 1 cup) frozen
  peas

1 medium onion, finely
  chopped

5 ml (1 tsp) olive oil

2.5 ml (½ tsp) turmeric

10 ml (2 tsp) Curry
  Powder (page 162)

2.5 ml (½ tsp) coriander

2.5 ml (½ tsp) salt or
  ½ chicken stock cube

5 ml (1 tsp) finely
  chopped or minced
  fresh ginger

pepper to taste

200 g (7 oz) low-fat plain
  yoghurt

12 sheets filo pastry

garnish: sliced
  cucumber, onion and
  tomato

Count on serving one or two samosas per person.

Method:

1. Boil, steam or microwave vegetables, except onion, until tender. Set aside to cool.
2. Sauté onion in oil until transparent but not brown. Combine with cooked vegetables in a bowl. Add spices. Check flavour and adjust to taste.
3. Using a pastry brush, spread a sheet of filo pastry lightly with yoghurt. Place a second sheet over the first and repeat the procedure. Place a third sheet over this, then cut the pastry in half lengthwise with a sharp knife.
4. Place a generous spoonful of the mixture on one end of the pastry rectangle and fold the filo diagonally to cover the filling. Continue to fold diagonally until all the pastry is folded, making sure that the mixture is totally enclosed.
5. Repeat this procedure until all the pastry is used.
6. Place samosas on a baking sheet. Bake in a preheated oven for about 15 minutes until brown. Serve with a garnish of sliced cucumber, onion and tomato.

Nutritional data per serve (for 4 serves): 1056 kJ (252 cal), CHO 44 g, Protein 11 g, Fat 4 g.

Preparation time: 1 hour. Cooking equipment: saucepan, frying pan, baking sheet. Oven temperature: 180 °C (350 °F, gas 4).

Appetizers and Snacks *Eat & Enjoy*

Salmon and Ricotta Loaf

Serves 8

440 g (15 oz) canned
  pink salmon
125 g (4 oz) ricotta cheese
juice of 1 lemon
5 ml (1 tsp) curry powder
good pinch of salt
6 spring onions
  (shallots), chopped
5 ml (1 tsp) gelatine
40 ml (8 tsp) hot water
1 French loaf (bread
  stick), wholemeal if
  available

Eat this on the day you make it because it does not keep. Use the soft bread from the centre of the loaf to make breadcrumbs.

Method:
1. Drain juice from salmon and discard skin and bones.
2. Mash the salmon and mix well with the cheese.
3. Add lemon juice, curry powder, salt and spring onions (shallots).
4. Melt gelatine in hot water, cool slightly, and stir into salmon mixture.
5. Chill in refrigerator for 30 minutes.
6. Cut the loaf into two equal lengths and remove the crusty ends. Hollow out with knife or spoon. Discard the soft centre.
7. Spoon filling into centres of the loaf and pack in firmly.
8. Wrap in foil and chill until ready to serve.
9. Slice in 2 cm (3/4 inch) pieces and serve.

Nutritional data per serve: 600 kJ (143 cal), CHO 6 g, Protein 15 g, Fat 7 g.
Preparation time: 45 minutes.

Mushroom Starter

**Makes about 125 g
(4 oz, 1 cup)**

60 g (2 oz, ¾ cup) finely
  chopped mushrooms
20 ml (4 tsp) chopped
  parsley
5 ml (1 tsp) finely
  snipped chives
good pinch ground
  oregano or 2.5 ml
  finely chopped fresh
  oregano
ground black pepper
60 ml (2 fl oz, ¼ cup) low-
  fat plain yoghurt
salt to taste

Method:
1. Mix all ingredients and refrigerate for 3 hours before serving.
2. Serve with fresh vegetable pieces, breads or biscuits (page 62).

Nutritional data per total: 282 kJ (67 cal), CHO 7 g, Protein 9 g, Fat 1 g.

Preparation time: 10 minutes.

Chinese Dumplings

Makes 4 serves
4 dumplings per serve

200 g (7 oz) lean minced
    pork
4 spring onions
    (shallots), finely
    chopped
250 g (8 oz) canned
    bamboo shoots, finely
    chopped
2.5 ml (½ tsp) minced
    ginger
20 ml (4 tsp) soy sauce
1 egg white
125 g (4 oz) won ton
    pastry squares
Sauce for dipping:
60 ml (2 fl oz, ¼ cup) soy
    sauce with a dash of
    chilli sauce

The won ton pastry squares used in this recipe are available from Oriental food stores and some supermarkets.

Method:
1. Combine all ingredients except won ton pastry squares.
2. Place about 5 ml (1 tsp) of mixture on to each won ton pastry square; keep unused pastry covered with a damp tea-towel while you are working.
3. Squeeze the pastry up around the filling to make a filled-bag shape.
4. Place dumplings in an oiled steamer and cook over boiling water for about 20 minutes.
5. Serve with dipping sauce.

To store: freeze after they are cooked.

Nutritional data per serve: 758 kJ (181 cal), CHO 23 g, Protein 17 g, Fat 2 g.

Preparation time: 45 minutes. Cooking equipment: steamer, saucepan.

Chicken Spread

Makes about 250 g
(8 oz, 1 cup)

150 g (5 oz, 1 cup)
    chopped, cooked
    chicken
60 g (2 oz, ½ cup)
    chopped almonds or
    walnuts
juice of ½ lemon
60 ml (2 fl oz, ¼ cup) low-
    fat plain yoghurt
pinch of mustard powder
20 ml (4 tsp) chopped
    onion
20 ml (4 tsp) chopped
    parsley

Method:
1. Blend all ingredients and refrigerate until ready to serve.
2. Serve on triangles of wholemeal toast, or roll in lettuce to make parcels.

To store: cover and refrigerate up to two days.

Nutritional data per total: 3185 kJ (761 cal), CHO 8 g, Protein 68 g, Fat 51 g.

Preparation time: 15 minutes.

Soups

Minestrone

Serves 4 – 6

2 medium onions

2 medium carrots

2 celery sticks

½ pepper (capsicum)

2 medium potatoes

125 g (4 oz) green beans,
   sliced

75 g (2½ oz, 1 cup)
   shredded cabbage

4 large tomatoes

10 ml (2 tsp) olive oil

200 g (7 oz, 1 cup) dried
   haricot or cannellini
   beans

900 ml (1½ pints,
   3¾ cups) water

3 bay leaves

2.5 ml (½ tsp) salt

good pinch of pepper

juice of ½ lemon

5 ml (1 tsp) dried mixed
   herbs or 10 ml (2 tsp)
   fresh mixed herbs

There are dozens of versions of this soup. This one has all the key ingredients of the classic recipe. To make this soup into a meal-in-one, you can add some cooked wholemeal macaroni just before serving. This provides even more carbohydrate.

Method:

1. Peel and chop vegetables.
2. Heat oil in a saucepan.
3. Add onions and cook until lightly browned.
4. Add carrots, celery, pepper (capsicum) and potatoes. Cook until lightly coloured.
5. Now add green beans, cabbage and tomatoes. Cook until just tender.
6. Add dried beans, water, herbs and lemon juice.
7. Simmer with lid on until beans are tender (about 1 hour).
8. Check seasoning and adjust to taste.
9. Serve with wholemeal bread.

To store: cover and refrigerate for up to three days.

Nutritional data per serve: 1105 kJ (264 cal), CHO 40 g, Protein 17 g, Fat 4 g.

Preparation time: 2 hours. Cooking equipment: large saucepan or stock pot.

Chicken Stock

*Makes about 900 ml
(1 ½ pints, 3¾ cups)*

---

2 medium onions, peeled
1 large carrot
2 celery sticks
1 x 1.5 kg (3 lb) boiling
    fowl
8 peppercorns
2 bay leaves
sprig of fresh or a good
    pinch of dried thyme
5 sprigs parsley
1.4 litres (2½ pints,
    6¼ cups) water
salt to taste

We've given storage options at the end of this recipe because chicken stock is so useful to have on hand. We use it in many other recipes, and it is superior to soup cubes or packet soups.

Method:
1. Wash and roughly chop the vegetables.
2. Place all the ingredients in a large saucepan.
3. Over medium heat, slowly bring to the boil. Skim off any scum that rises to the surface. Reduce heat, cover and simmer gently for 3 hours.
4. Strain the soup through a sieve. Reserve the meat for another dish. Discard skin, bones and vegetables.
5. Chill in refrigerator overnight and then skim off any congealed fat. Use in recipes requiring chicken stock, or reheat and serve in cups as a nutritious hot beverage.

To vary: Chicken Soup with Noodles or Rice – just before serving, add about 170 g (6 oz, 1/2 cup) cooked vermicelli or boiled rice to the hot soup.

To store stock: keep in a sealed container in refrigerator. Clarified stock will keep for a week or two if re-boiled every few days. Freeze in an ice cube tray. Store cubes in a freezer bag for convenience.

Nutritional data per serve: negligible.

Preparation time: about 3 hours. Cooking equipment: large saucepan.

Foreground left: Harlequin Salad, right Fettuccine Salmon Salad with Fruity Rice Salad behind it. At the back, filled pitta bread.

Corn Chowder

Serves 4

10 ml (2 tsp) margarine

1 large onion, peeled and
   chopped

2 medium potatoes,
   peeled

1 chicken stock cube

pinch of mixed dried
   herbs or 2.5 ml (½ tsp)
   fresh mixed herbs

pepper to taste

440 g (15 oz) canned
   sweetcorn kernels

125 ml (4 fl oz, ½ cup)
   water

350 ml (12 fl oz, 1½ cups)
   skimmed or low-fat
   milk

20 ml (4 tsp) cornflour
   (cornstarch)

Method:

1. Melt margarine in saucepan. Add onion and cook over low heat until translucent.
2. Cut potatoes into small dice and add to onion in saucepan.
3. Add stock cube and herbs, pepper, sweetcorn and its liquid and the water.
4. Cover and simmer until potatoes are tender (about 15 minutes). Now add the milk.
5. In a small bowl, blend cornflour (cornstarch) with a little water to a smooth paste. Add to the soup.
6. Bring to the boil, then simmer until slightly thickened, stirring from time to time.
7. Sprinkle with parsley and serve.

Nutritional data per serve: 1032 kJ (246 cal), CHO 44 g, Protein 8 g, Fat 4 g.

Preparation time: 45 minutes. Cooking equipment: large saucepan.

Foreground: buttered Date and Walnut Loaf, centre right Apple and Apricot Slice with a basket of Chris's Cookies beside it. Banana Muffins at the top.

Gazpacho

Serves 4

---

1 small cucumber, peeled

3 spring onions (shallots)

½ red pepper (capsicum)

½ green pepper
  (capsicum)

2 celery sticks

4 medium ripe tomatoes
  or 410 g (14 oz) canned
  tomatoes

1 medium onion

900 ml (1½ pints,
  3¾ cups) Chicken Stock
  (page 72)

250 ml (8 fl oz, 1 cup)
  tomato juice

20 ml (4 tsp) coarsely
  ground black pepper

5 – 10 ml (1 – 2 tsp)
  Tabasco, according to
  taste

garnish: chopped parsley

This delightful Spanish soup can be presented hot or chilled.

Method:

1. Finely chop half the cucumber, three spring onions (shallots), a quarter of each red and green pepper (capsicum), a stick of celery and one tomato. Set aside.
2. Roughly chop all remaining vegetables and place in food processor with chicken stock, tomato juice, pepper and Tabasco and blend until smooth.
3. Add finely chopped vegetables, mix and chill well.
4. Serve, garnished with chopped parsley.

To store: cover and refrigerate for up to three days.

Nutritional data per serve: 195 kJ (47 cal), CHO 8 g, Protein 3 g, Fat trace.

Preparation time: 25 minutes. Cooking equipment: food processor or blender.

Orange Borscht

Serves 4

375 g (12 oz, 3 cups)
  peeled and grated
  beetroot
750 ml (1¼ pints,
  3 cups) Chicken Stock
  (page 72)
250 ml (8 fl oz, 1 cup)
  unsweetened orange
  juice
250 ml (8 fl oz, 1 cup)
  unsweetened tomato
  juice
1 sprig fresh thyme or a
  good pinch of dried
  thyme
ground black pepper
garnish: chopped parsley

Beetroot soup (borscht) is eastern European in origin and would, traditionally, have been eaten accompanied by plain boiled potatoes. You can also add a spoonful of low-fat plain yoghurt to each bowl just before you serve the soup.

Method:

1. Place beetroot and stock in saucepan and bring to the boil. Simmer for 20 minutes.
2. Strain stock into a clean saucepan and add 125 g (4 oz, 1 cup) of the cooked beetroot. Discard the remaining beetroot.
3. Add the juices, thyme and pepper.
4. Bring to the boil and remove sprig of thyme.
5. Serve in bowls, sprinkled with chopped parsley.

To store: cover and refrigerate for up to three days.

Nutritional data per serve: 263 kJ (63 cal), CHO 13 g, Protein 2 g, Fat trace.

Preparation time: 30 minutes. Cooking equipment: 2 large saucepans.

Chinese Chicken and Sweetcorn Soup

Serves 4

10 ml (2 tsp) oil
2 chicken fillets, finely
  sliced
2 garlic cloves, crushed
5 ml (1 tsp) chopped
  fresh ginger
1¾ pints (1 litre) Chicken
  Stock (page 72)
410 g (14 oz) canned
  creamed sweetcorn
1 egg, lightly beaten
garnish: chopped spring
  onions (shallots)

Method:

1. Place oil in saucepan and heat until moderately hot.
2. Now lightly brown sliced chicken, garlic and ginger. Don't overcook.
3. Add stock and bring to the boil.
4. Add creamed corn and simmer for 10 minutes.
5. Remove from heat when ready to serve, then quickly stir in egg to make long strands.
6. Garnish with chopped spring onions (shallots).

To store: cover and refrigerate for up to three days.

Nutritional data per serve: 1029 kJ (246 cal), CHO 26 g, Protein 17 g, Fat 8 g.

Preparation time: 45 minutes. Cooking equipment: saucepan.

Hot and Sour Soup

Serves 4

3 chicken fillets

45 ml (1 ½ fl oz) white
 vinegar

10 ml (2 tsp) oil

125 g (4 oz) firm tofu
 (soybean curd), cut into
 small cubes

900 ml (1 ¼ pints,
 3¾ cups) Chicken Stock
 (page 72)

½ medium red pepper
 (capsicum), cut into
 thin strips

125 g (4 oz) button
 mushrooms

125 g (4 oz) canned
 bamboo shoots,
 drained

4 spring onions
 (shallots), chopped

40 ml (8 tsp) cornflour
 (cornstarch)

1 egg

garnish: soy sauce

Method:

1. With a sharp knife, slice chicken very finely.
2. Place chicken slices in a bowl with the vinegar.
3. Place oil in heavy saucepan and heat on high. Add tofu and stir-fry until tender (about 3 minutes). Remove from saucepan.
4. Pour chicken stock into saucepan with pepper (capsicum), mushrooms, bamboo shoots and spring onions (shallots). Heat to boiling, cover and simmer for 10 minutes or until vegetables are tender.
5. Add chicken and tofu, heat to boiling.
6. Mix cornflour (cornstarch) with a small amount of water until smooth.
7. Slowly stir cornflour (cornstarch) mixture into boiling soup.
8. Cook, stirring constantly, until slightly thickened. Remove from heat.
9. Beat egg in a small bowl.
10. Slowly pour egg into soup, stirring quickly until egg swirls and has just set.
11. Spoon soup into individual bowls.
12. To each bowl add a dash of soy sauce.

To store: cover and refrigerate for up to three days.

Nutritional data per serve: 1328 kJ (317 cal), CHO 8 g, Protein 28 g, Fat 19 g.

Preparation time: 30 minutes. Cooking equipment: large saucepan.

Hungarian Soup

Serves 4

---

750 ml (1¼ pints,
   3 cups) chicken stock
750 g (2½ oz, 1 cup)
   finely shredded red
   cabbage
3 small onions, thinly
   sliced
1 garlic clove, crushed
2 large tomatoes, peeled
   and quartered
1 large apple, peeled and
   chopped
coarsely ground black
   pepper, to taste
good pinch of ground
   allspice
garnish: snipped chives

This is a simple, filling and aromatic soup with just a hint of sweetness; ideal for cold winter nights. Eaten with wholemeal bread, it makes a warming supper. For the stock, either use good quality cubes or make your own according to our recipe on page 72.

Method:

1. Place stock in a large saucepan and bring to the boil.
2. Add all other ingredients.
3. Cover and simmer for 30 minutes.
4. Serve, garnished with a sprinkling of snipped chives.

To store: cover and refrigerate for up to three days.

Nutritional data per serve: 213 kJ (51 cal), CHO 10 g, Protein 2 g, Fat trace.

Preparation time: 45 minutes. Cooking equipment: saucepan.

Broccoli and Sweetcorn Soup

Serves 4

---

1 large head broccoli
450 ml (¾ pint, 2 cups)
   Chicken Stock (page 72)
440 g (15 oz) canned
   creamed sweetcorn
1 celery stick, finely
   chopped
6 spring onions
   (shallots), finely sliced
2.5 ml (½ tsp) salt
   (optional)
pepper to taste
garnish: snipped chives

Note the high proportion of complex carbohydrate in this delicious soup. Use Chicken Stock recipe on page 72 for a superior result.

Method:

1. Break the broccoli into florets and cook it in stock until tender (about 10 minutes).
2. Blend until smooth in food processor.
3. Add creamed sweetcorn, celery, spring onions (shallots) and seasonings.
4. Reheat and serve, garnished with snipped chives.

To store: cover and refrigerate for up to three days.

Nutritional data per serve: 760 kJ (182 cal), CHO 30 g, Protein 9 g, Fat 3 g.

Preparation time: 30 minutes. Cooking equipment: saucepan, food processor or blender.

Curried Carrot and Rice Soup

Serves 4

4 medium carrots,
   washed and chopped
1 onion, chopped
450 ml (¾ pint, 2 cups)
   water
100 g (3½ oz, ½ cup)
   brown rice
250 ml (8 fl oz, 1 cup)
   water
40 ml (8 tsp) finely
   chopped parsley
5 ml (1 tsp) curry powder
2.5 ml (½ tsp) salt
2.5 ml (½ tsp) black
   pepper
350 ml (12 fl oz,
   1½ cups) skimmed
   milk
garnish: paprika

Although we advocate as little salt as possible in our cooking, it seems to bring out the taste of all the other ingredients in curries.

Method:

1. Cook carrots and onions in 450 ml (3/4 pint, 2 cups) water until tender. Set aside in the cooking liquid.
2. In the second saucepan, cook brown rice in 250 ml (8 fl oz, 1 cup) water until tender (about 20 – 25 minutes). Drain and discard the cooking liquid.
3. Combine carrots, onions and their cooking liquid in food processor or blender until smooth.
4. Add parsley, curry powder, salt, pepper, cooked rice and milk.
5. Return to saucepan and heat until just starting to boil.
6. Remove from the heat and serve, garnished with paprika.

Nutritional data per serve: 668 kJ (160 cal), CHO 31 g, Protein 7 g, Fat 1 g.

Preparation time: 1 hour. Cooking equipment: 2 saucepans, food processor or blender.

Pork and Vegetable Noodle Soup

Serves 4

200 g (7 oz) bacon bones
1 litre (1¾ pints,
   4 cups) water
250 g (8 oz) pork fillet,
   diced
1 medium carrot, grated
2 celery sticks, chopped
½ parsnip, grated
½ turnip, grated
1 medium leek, chopped
40 ml (8 tsp) chopped
   parsley
2.5 ml (½ tsp) black
   pepper
90 g (3 oz) fresh noodles

The noodles add complex carbohydrate to this nutritious soup.

Method:

1. Place bacon bones and water in saucepan and bring to the boil. Simmer for 1 hour. Strain stock and discard the bones.
2. Heat saucepan and dry-fry pork fillet until browned.
3. Add pork, carrot, celery, parsnip, turnip, leek, parsley and black pepper to stock.
4. Cook until meat and vegetables are tender.
5. Add noodles and cook for a further 5 – 10 minutes or until noodles are tender, too.
6. Spoon into individual bowls and garnish with chopped spring onions (shallots).

Nutritional data per serve: 633 kJ (151 cal), CHO 16 g, Protein 18 g, Fat 2 g.

Preparation time: 2 hours. Cooking equipment: 2 saucepans.

Beef and Bean Soup

Serves 4

---

250 g (8 oz) lean minced
  beef
1 medium onion, diced
1 small clove garlic
2 celery sticks, diced
410 g (14 oz) canned
  tomatoes
20 ml (4 tsp) tomato paste
750 ml (1¼ pints,
  3 cups) water
2.5 ml (½ tsp) dried
  oregano or 5 ml
  (1 tsp) fresh
2.5 ml (½ tsp) paprika
2.5 ml (½ tsp) ground
  cumin
10 ml (2 tsp) white
  vinegar
440 g (15 oz) canned
  kidney beans, drained

This hearty soup only needs plenty of wholemeal bread to make it into a meal-in-one.

Method:

1. Dry-fry meat, add onion and garlic and cook until juices evaporate and beef is well browned.
2. Add celery, tomatoes, tomato paste, water, oregano, paprika, cumin and vinegar.
3. Bring to the boil. Add beans and reduce heat to low, cover and simmer for 30 minutes.

To store: cover and refrigerate for up to three days.

Nutritional data per serve: 844 kJ (202 cal), CHO 17 g, Protein 26 g, Fat 3 g.

Preparation time: 1 hour. Cooking equipment: saucepan.

Souper Douper Pumpkin Soup

Serves 4

---

750 g (1½ lb) pumpkin,
  peeled and cut into
  pieces
1 large leek, sliced
750 ml (1½ pints,
  3 cups) chicken stock
10 ml (2 tsp) mixed dried
  herbs
2.5 ml (½ tsp) coarsely
  ground black pepper
good pinch of grated
  nutmeg
good pinch of ground
  coriander
2.5 ml (½ tsp) salt
40 ml (8 tsp) lemon juice
40 ml (8 tsp) chopped
  parsley

Method:

1. Place all ingredients except lemon juice and parsley in a saucepan.
2. Bring to the boil and simmer until pumpkin is tender (about 20 minutes).
3. Cool slightly, blend in food processor or blender until smooth.
4. Add lemon juice and parsley. Check seasoning.
5. Serve with Herby Corn Muffins (page 185).

To store: cover and refrigerate for up to three days.

Nutritional data per serve: 342 kJ (82 cal), CHO 14 g, Protein 5 g, Fat 1 g.

Preparation time: 1 hour. Cooking equipment: saucepan, food processor or blender.

Entrées and Light Meals

Wholemeal Beef and Bean Burritos

Serves 4

Filling:

500 g (1 lb) lean minced
   steak
1 medium onion,
   chopped
1 beef stock cube or
   2.5 ml (½ tsp) salt
2.5 ml (½ tsp) pepper
150 g (5 oz) tomato paste
100 ml (3½ fl oz) water
Tabasco to taste
juice of ½ lemon
410 g (14 oz) canned red
   kidney beans, rinsed
   and drained
garnish: shredded lettuce
   and finely chopped
   onion
Tortillas:
125 g (4 oz, 1 cup) each,
   wholemeal flour and
   plain flour
10 ml (2 tsp) baking
   powder
2.5 ml (½ tsp) salt
250 ml (8 fl oz, 1 cup)
   warm water

Method:

Filling:

1. Dry-fry meat until lightly browned. Add onion and continue to sauté until browned.
2. Add crumbled stock cube or salt, pepper, tomato paste, Tabasco and lemon juice. Stir until well combined. Add kidney beans and mix in well. Bring to the boil, turn down the heat and simmer for 10 – 15 minutes until the meat is cooked.
3. Add extra water (if necessary) to make a thick sauce.
4. Keep meat and bean mixture warm until tortillas are ready or allow to cool, refrigerate and reheat when needed.

Tortillas:

5. Sift flours, baking powder and salt.
6. Gradually stir in warm water to form a dough.
7. Turn dough on to floured board and knead until smooth. Cover with cling film (plastic wrap) and allow to rest for 15 – 20 minutes.
8. Cut into twelve equal pieces. Shape each into a ball.
9. Flatten each ball into a 10 – 12 cm (4 – 5 inch) patty, roll into a very thin round about 20 – 23 cm (8 – 9 inches) making sure dough and rolling pin are well floured to prevent sticking.
10. Heat frying pan. Place each tortilla on dry surface of frying pan. As blisters appear, press gently with egg slice or spatula. When underside is brown, turn over and cook until blisters have formed on other side and tortilla is lightly browned.
11. Lift on to tray covered with a damp tea-towel. Fold tea-towel to cover tortilla.
12. Repeat until all tortillas are cooked.
13. Place some hot filling on each tortilla and roll up.
14. Serve immediately, garnished with lettuce and onion. Tortillas should be eaten with the fingers.

Nutritional data per serve: 2233 kJ (533 cal), CHO 66 g, Protein 59 g, Fat 7g.
Preparation time: 2 hours. Cooking equipment: frying pan.

Prosciutto and Melon

Serves 4

½ ripe cantaloup (rock
  melon), peeled and
  seeded
12 paper-thin slices
  prosciutto
4 lettuce leaves

Method

1. Cut the melon in two and then cut each half into six evenly shaped pieces.
2. Wrap each piece of melon in a slice of proscuitto and secure with a cocktail stick (toothpick).
3. Arrange lettuce leaves on four individual plates and top each with three pieces of melon and prosciutto. Serve chilled.

To vary: use honeydew melon instead of cantaloup (rock melon). Try using smoked pork or smoked beef instead of prosciutto (Parma ham).

Nutritional data per serve: 189 kJ (45 cal), CHO 1 g, Protein 5 g, Fat 2 g.
Preparation time: 15 minutes.

Harlequin Noodle Salad

Serves 4

150 g (5 oz, 1 cup) shell
  pasta (noodles)
150 g (5 oz, 1 cup) cooked,
  diced chicken fillets
60 g (2 oz, ½ cup) diced
  celery
1 small green and
  1 small red pepper
  (capsicum), chopped
4 spring onions (shallots)
  chopped
20 ml (4 tsp) chopped
  parsley
90 g (3 oz, ½ cup)
  sultanas
black pepper to taste
dressing: ½ quantity
  Curry Dressing
  (page 160)
garnish: 4 lettuce cups

Make this the day before you want to serve it, so the flavour can develop.

Method:

1. Place pasta (noodles) in saucepan of boiling water. Cook until tender and then drain.
2. Combine cooked pasta (noodles), diced chicken, celery, peppers (capsicums), spring onions (shallots), parsley, sultanas and black pepper.
3. Mix in the curry dressing.
4. Refrigerate for at least 1 hour.
5. Serve in lettuce cups.

To store: keep in airtight container in refrigerator for up to two days.

Nutritional data per serve: 950 kJ (227 cal), CHO 34 g, Protein 16 g, Fat 3 g.

Preparation time: 1½ hours plus preparation time for dressing.
Cooking equipment: saucepan.

Crêpes and Pancakes

*Serves 6
(makes 12 large or 24
small crêpes)*

---

*125 g (4 oz, 1 cup)
  wholemeal or plain
  flour or half-and-half
3 eggs, lightly beaten
10 ml (2 tsp) oil or
  melted butter
350 ml (12 fl oz, 1½ cups)
  skimmed milk*

Crêpes are small, very thin pancakes; the raw batter is thinner than for traditional pancakes.

Pancakes (see opposite) make a large, hearty wrapping for a variety of fillings. The cooked pancake should be less than 3 mm (1/8 inch) thick.

Both crêpes and pancakes are simple to make and very versatile. With either savoury or sweet fillings, use them for entrées, main courses, desserts or snacks.

You will find that crêpes made entirely with wholemeal flour tend to be rather heavy. A half-and-half combination makes a nutritious and tasty version.

Method:

1. If using a food processor or blender, add all ingredients at once and process until smooth. If working by hand, sift flour into a bowl (if using wholemeal flour, add any wheat husks left in sieve to the sifted flour). Make a well in the flour. Slowly add the beaten eggs, stirring continually to draw the ingredients together and prevent lumps from forming. Mix oil or melted butter with milk. Slowly add to flour mixture, stirring continuously to form a thin, smooth consistency like that of thin pouring cream. If too thick, add more milk, a little at a time, until you have the right consistency.

2. Transfer batter to a jug and leave to stand in a cool place for at least an hour. If the mixture has thickened, add more milk, a little at a time, to obtain the consistency of thin pouring cream.

3. Lightly grease a crêpe or heavy-bottomed frying pan and heat until very hot but not smoking. Pour in 45 – 90 ml (1½ – 3 fl oz) of batter depending on size of pan; tilt pan to spread batter evenly.

4. When fine bubbles appear on the surface of the crêpe and it appears dry, use an egg slice or spatula to flip it over; cook the other side for about 5 seconds until pale golden brown.

5. Repeat these steps for the remainder of the batter, brushing the pan with a little oil between crêpes and stacking them as they are cooked. Keep them covered with a damp tea towel until you need them.

Use any of the filling mixtures on page 84, or create your own. Crêpes can be filled and then served rolled up or folded in half or in quarters.

To store: you may prepare crêpes and pancakes ahead of time. Cover and refrigerate them for up to two days, or pack in freezer bags, with a layer of waxed paper or cling film (plastic wrap) between each crêpe, and freeze.

Nutritional data per serve: 968 kJ (231 cal), CHO 29 g, Protein 12 g, Fat 7 g.
Preparation time: batter 10 minutes, standing time for raw batter 1 hour, cooking time 20 minutes.
Cooking equipment: jug, crêpe pan or small frying pan.

Pancakes

Serves 4 – 5 (makes 8 – 10 pancakes)

90 g (3 oz, ¼ cup) wholemeal or plain flour or half-and-half
1 egg
about 350 ml (12 fl oz, 1 ½ cups) skimmed milk

This is a traditional recipe. Pancakes are larger and heavier-textured than crêpes. The pancakes should be about the size of a dinner plate and about 3 mm (1/8 inch) thick. The same guidelines we set out at the start of the crêpe recipe apply here.

Method:

Exactly as for crêpes.

To store: as for crêpes.

Nutritional data per serve: 778 kJ (186 cal), CHO 26 g, Protein 9 g, Fat 5 g.
Preparation time: batter 10 minutes, standing time for raw batter 1 hour, cooking time 20 minutes.
Cooking equipment: jug, small frying pan.

Savoury Fillings for Crêpes or Pancakes

Allow three crêpes or two pancakes per serve. Fill pancakes with any of the fillings that follow, and top with low-fat plain yoghurt or ricotta cheese or a fine sprinkling of Parmesan cheese. Serve the filled pancakes hot, accompanied by a crisp, green salad.

Ham and asparagus	Diced lean ham and cooked asparagus spears or pieces tossed in Cheese Sauce (page 152).
Mushroom and onion	Sliced mushrooms and onions cooked in a frying pan brushed with oil and tossed in White Sauce (page 151).
Ratatouille	Ratatouille Sauce (page 154) topped with grated low-fat hard cheese.
Spinach	Cooked, chopped spinach mixed with ricotta cheese, sautéed spring onions (shallots), chopped basil and pine nuts.
Seafood	500 g (1 lb) mixed seafood cooked in one quantity of Tomato and Basil Sauce (page 155).
Chicken and avocado	Two sliced, cooked chicken fillets and one sliced avocado tossed in one quantity Cheese Sauce (page 152).
Savoury beef	500 g (1 lb) lean minced beef cooked in one quantity of Tomato and Basil Sauce (page 155). Fill crêpes or pancakes and top with low-fat plain yoghurt or ricotta cheese, or a fine sprinkling of Parmesan cheese.
Steak and onion	Slice 500 g (1 lb) fillet steak into very thin strips, and marinate in 40 ml (8 tsp) Worcestershire sauce and one crushed garlic clove for 10 minutes. Sauté beef in 10 ml (2 tsp) oil for 3 minutes. Add one large onion, sliced, and sauté for another 2 minutes. Add 60 ml (2 fl oz, 1/4 cup) red wine, and simmer for 1 – 2 minutes. Thicken with 20 ml (4 tsp) cornflour (cornstarch) blended with 40 ml (8 tsp) water. Fill pancakes and serve them topped with low-fat plain yoghurt and a sprinkling of chopped parsley.

Red kidney bean and corn

Sauté one medium red pepper (capsicum), finely diced, and one medium onion, finely chopped, in 60 ml (2 fl oz, 1/4 cup) water for about 3 minutes until soft. Add 200 g (7 oz, 1 cup) drained canned red kidney beans, 170 g (6 oz, 1 cup) drained canned sweetcorn kernels, 40 ml (8 tsp) tomato paste, a good pinch of ground oregano and a small pinch chilli powder. Simmer gently for 5 – 10 minutes until the liquid has almost evaporated. Fill the pancakes and roll them up. Sprinkle with low-fat grated cheese and grill to melt the cheese topping.

Bombay Burgers with Cucumber and Yoghurt Sauce

Serves 4
(makes 12 patties)

200 g (7 oz, 1 cup) dried red lentils

1 large potato, cut into pieces

1 medium onion, finely chopped

15 g (½ oz, ¼ cup) shredded coconut

20 ml (4 tsp) sesame seeds

20 ml (4 tsp) plain flour

5 ml (1 tsp) curry powder

5 ml (1 tsp) finely chopped fresh ginger

2.5 ml (½ tsp) salt

good pinch of pepper

10 ml (2 tsp) lemon juice

45 – 60 g (1½ – 2 oz, ¾ – 1 cup) wheatgerm

garnish: sliced onion rings

1 quantity of Cucumber and Yoghurt Sauce (page 156)

Method:

1. Soak lentils in water for 2 hours.
2. Rinse, cover with water in a saucepan and simmer for about 30 minutes until tender. Add potato 10 minutes into the cooking time. Alternatively, place the lentils in a bowl with water and microwave on High for 20 minutes or until tender. Add the potatoes 10 minutes into the cooking time.
3. Drain any liquid from lentils and potato and mash thoroughly. Add onion, coconut, sesame seeds, flour, spices and lemon juice.
4. Allow to cool (preferably chill).
5. Shape into patties and coat with wheatgerm.
6. Bake in a preheated oven on a lightly oiled baking sheet for 10 – 15 minutes, or cook in a frying pan lightly brushed with oil, taking care not to burn wheatgerm.
7. Serve hot, garnished with onion rings and with Cucumber and Yoghurt Sauce.

Nutritional data per serve: 838 kJ (200 cal), CHO 22 g, Protein 10 g, Fat 8 g.

Preparation time: 1 hour plus preparation time for sauce. Cooking equipment: saucepan, baking sheet or frying pan. Oven temperature: 190 °C (375 °F, gas 5).

Pasties (and Filo Rolls)

Serves 4

200 g (7 oz) rump,
   porterhouse or fillet
   steak
1 potato, finely diced
1 medium carrot, finely
   diced
1 small turnip, finely
   diced
1 small onion, finely
   diced
good pinch of white
   pepper
good pinch of dried
   mixed herbs
40 ml (8 tsp) finely
   chopped parsley
1 quantity Wholemeal
   Pastry (page 186)
20 ml (4 tsp) water
40 ml (8 tsp) skimmed
   milk for glazing

As a main course, serve pasties with vegetables and Tomato and Basil Sauce (page 155). They also make a wonderful light lunch or meal, served with salad.

Method:

1. Cut meat into small cubes, about 12 mm (1/2 inch) square.
2. In a bowl, combine meat, diced vegetables, pepper and herbs.
3. Divide pastry into four portions. Roll out each portion to about the size of a saucer.
4. Divide the meat mixture between the rounds, placing meat slightly off the centre of each round.
5. Brush the edges of the pastry with a little water. Fold pastry over, in half, to make a pasty shape.
6. Use the back of a fork to crimp the edges of the pasties firmly.
7. Place the finished pasties on a lightly greased baking sheet. Prick the top of each pasty three times with a fork. Brush the surface of each pasty with a little skimmed milk.
8. Bake in a preheated oven for 35 minutes or until browned.

To freeze: prepare the pasties to Step 6 and place in freezer bags or other suitable container. Defrost before baking as above.

Nutritional data per serve: 2374 kJ (567 cal), CHO 56 g, Protein 22 g, Fat 28 g.

Preparation time: 1½ hours. Cooking equipment: baking sheet. Oven temperature: 200 °C (400 °F, gas 6).

Filo Rolls

(makes 4 rolls)

This variation of pasties keeps the fat content down – twelve sheets of filo pastry are all you need to make four rolls.

Method:

1. Precook the meat and vegetables by combining them in a saucepan with 125 ml (4 fl oz, 1/2 cup) water and simmering them for 10 minutes. Drain.

2. Use three sheets of filo pastry per roll, folding each sheet in half to make six layers. Brush skimmed milk between the layers of the filo pastry. Divide the meat mixture into four, place a serving on each portion of filo, then roll them into parcels. Brush the inner edges of the filo with a little skimmed milk and press down gently to seal. Glaze the tops of the rolls lightly with skimmed milk. Bake in a preheated oven for 15 – 20 minutes, or until crisp and lightly brown.

To store: cover and refrigerate for up to two days. Reheat slowly but thoroughly. If you want to freeze them, do so before you bake them; thaw and bake them as above when required.

Nutritional data per serve: 860 kJ (205 cal), CHO 28 g, Protein 16 g, Fat 3 g.

Gado Gado

Serves 4

90 g (3 oz, 1 cup) bean shoots

100 g (3½ oz, 1 cup) green beans, strings removed

225 g (7½ oz, 1½ cups) broccoli florets

100 g (3½ oz, 1 cup) carrot slices

90 g (3 oz, 1 cup) cabbage, diced

1 medium green pepper (capsicum), sliced

6 – 10 mangetout (snow peas)

2 tomatoes, cut into wedges

2 onions, cut into wedges

1 small cucumber, peeled and diced

2 hard-boiled eggs, cut into quarters

You have free reign with this recipe to add or change vegetables according to season or taste.

Method:

1. Half-fill a medium saucepan with water and bring to a rapid boil. Plunge the vegetables, except the tomatoes and cucumber, one variety at a time, into the boiling water for no more than 1 minute, or until the colour intensifies, or microwave with 40 ml (8 tsp) water on High for 2 minutes. Quickly remove the blanched vegetables from the water, place in the colander and immediately flush with cold, running water; this preserves the colour and crispness. Bring water back to the boil before blanching each type of vegetable.
2. Arrange all the ingredients on a platter.
3. Serve as an appetizer or entrée at either room temperature or chilled with cooked brown rice and a dish of warm Peanut (Saté) Sauce (page 152).

To store: cover and refrigerate for no more than one day.

Nutritional data per serve: 433 kJ (103 cal), CHO 10 g, Protein 9 g, Fat 3 g.

Preparation time: 30 minutes. Cooking equipment: medium saucepan, large saucepan.

Spinach Ravioli with Fresh Tomato Sauce

Serves 4

6 large ripe tomatoes,
    roughly chopped
5 ml (1 tsp) sugar
5 ml (1 tsp) chopped
    fresh basil or 2.5 ml
    (½ tsp) dried basil
pinch of tarragon
375 g (12 oz) fresh
    spinach ravioli
60 g (2 oz) low-fat hard
    cheese, grated

You can use tortellini instead of ravioli.

Method:

1. Place tomatoes, sugar and herbs in saucepan and simmer gently until mixture forms a thick sauce.
2. While tomatoes are cooking, fill a second saucepan to three-quarters with cold water and rapidly bring to the boil. Add ravioli and cook until tender. Drain.
3. Pour sauce over ravioli and mix gently.
4. Sprinkle with cheese.

Nutritional data per serve: 1307 kJ (312 cal), CHO 51 g, Protein 15 g, Fat 5 g.

Preparation time: 45 minutes. Cooking equipment: 2 saucepans.

Fish and Seafood

The beauty of fish and seafood is that they have plenty of protein, vitamins and minerals and little fat. This gives them an energy value less than an equivalent serving of meat and makes fish and seafood an invaluable and delicious part of your regular meal plan.

Cooking fish and seafood

Baking

Whole fish (large or small), cutlets or fish fillets are all equally good cooked this way. Place the fish in a shallow casserole and flavour it to taste, for instance with a sliced onion, a bay leaf, herbs of your choice, a few peppercorns and a little salt (optional). Then pour over the fish 125 – 250 ml (4 – 8 fl oz, ½ – 1 cup) of liquid, depending on the amount of fish. The liquid can be low-fat milk, wine or tomato juice. Bake, covered, in a preheated oven at 180 °C (350 °F, gas 4) for about 15 – 20 minutes or until the fish flakes when you test it with a fork.

Alternatively, place the fish on foil, sprinkle with lemon juice and herbs, seal and then cook as above without any additional liquid.

Grilling

Allow 5 – 8 minutes for fillets, cutlets, kebabs or small fish; 10 minutes for medium-sized whole fish and 15 – 20 minutes for large whole fish. Watch the fish carefully while it grills, turning it once or twice, or it will overcook and dry out.

We have given some lovely marinade recipes in this book which you can use to flavour the fish before and as a baste while cooking. Grilled fish is delicious cooked with no more than a sprinkling of herbs, lemon juice, black pepper and a little salt, if desired.

Poaching

With this method the fish cooks in a flavoured, simmering liquid. Place the fish in a shallow saucepan with a lid, add just enough liquid (milk, stock or wine, or a combination of any two of these) to cover the fish barely and then season it to taste. You can, for instance, add sliced onion, bay leaf, peppercorns, ground black pepper, parsley and a sliced carrot, which will give you a wonderfully flavoursome result. Add salt if you like.

Cover and simmer gently on the hob for 5 – 8 minutes if you are using thin fillets, or for 10 minutes if you are using thicker pieces. Use the test of flaking the fish with a fork to check when it's ready and take it off the heat immediately. Use the poaching liquid as the base for a sauce.

Microwaving fish

Fish is excellent cooked in the microwave. Place fish in the microwave dish, add 60 ml (2 fl oz, 1/4 cup) of liquid such as wine, stock or low-fat milk, flavour as for poaching or baking above, cover with clingfilm (plastic wrap) and cook the fish on High. Allow 3 minutes for small fillets, 5 – 7 minutes for larger fillets or small whole fish and 10 – 12 minutes for large whole fish. Arrange the seafood in a single layer in a shallow dish. Cover with clingfilm (plastic wrap) and cook on Medium until opaque (about 3 – 4 minutes). Leave to stand, covered, for 5 minutes before serving.

Fish with Various Sauces

Grill four fillets of white fish such as plaice, whiting or haddock on both sides until cooked through (about 8 – 10 minutes). Alternatively, cover and microwave on Medium-high for 4 – 6 minutes. Serve topped with a sauce such as:

Green Champagne (page 151)   *Black Bean* (page 154)

Ratatouille (page 154)   *Sweet and Sour* (page 157).

Piquant Fish in Foil

Serves 4

4 large fillets of fish (cod,
 haddock or plaice), or
 small whole fish (trout)
10 ml (2 tsp) finely
 chopped fresh tarragon
 or 2.5 ml (½ tsp) dried
20 ml (4 tsp) very finely
 chopped parsley
 (optional)
coarsely ground black
 pepper to taste
1 medium onion, thinly
 sliced
1 lemon, thinly sliced
juice of 1 lemon
40 ml (8 tsp) dry white
 wine (optional)

This is a wonderful way to prepare fresh fish. Serve it with jacket potatoes and a crisp salad.

Method:

1. Use four pieces of foil large enough to wrap the fish portions completely. Lightly grease the foil.
2. Place the fish on the pieces of foil. Sprinkle each fillet or small fish with the herbs and black pepper. Arrange several onion rings on top of each portion and top with one or two slices of lemon.
3. Mix lemon juice and white wine, if using, and pour over the fish.
4. Wrap each portion in foil, sealing along the top, so that the juices are not lost during cooking or when opening the foil.
5. Place the foil parcels, sealed-side up, on a baking sheet. Bake in a preheated oven or barbecue for 30 minutes.
6. Open foil along the sealing edge and serve immediately.

Nutritional data per serve: 623 kJ (149 cal), CHO 2 g, Protein 27 g, Fat 3 g.

Preparation time: 30 – 40 minutes. Cooking equipment: baking sheet. Oven temperature: 180 °C (350 °F, gas 4). Barbecue: glowing coals.

Fish in Orange Sauce

Serves 4

juice of 2 oranges
juice of 1 lemon
5 ml (1 tsp) margarine
good pinch of coarsely
 ground black pepper
4 fish fillets
small quantity of plain
 flour

Method:

1. Place juices, margarine and pepper in a frying pan.
2. Cook until slightly reduced.
3. Dust fish with flour.
4. Add to sauce and poach until just cooked, turning once.
5. Lift on to serving plates. Spoon sauce over.

Nutritional data per serve: 693 kJ (166 cal), CHO 4 g, Protein 27 g, Fat 4 g.

Preparation time: 15 minutes. Cooking equipment: frying pan.

Curried Tuna and Rice Casserole

Serves 4

410 g (14 oz) canned
   tuna in brine
juice of 1 lemon
125 g (4 oz) brown rice
Sauce:
2 small onions, diced
15 ml (3 tsp) curry
   powder
40 ml (8 tsp) wholemeal
   flour
750 ml (1 ¼ pints,
   3 cups) skimmed milk
2 slices wholemeal
   bread, crumbed

Replace tuna with salmon if you prefer.

Method:

1. Mix tuna and lemon juice in a bowl.
2. Cook brown rice in boiling water.
3. Drain rice and combine with the tuna mixture.
4. Dry-fry onion and curry powder in a saucepan.
5. Combine flour with a little of the milk to make a smooth paste.
6. Add remaining milk to onions and curry powder and bring to the boil. Remove from heat and add the flour paste.
7. Return to heat and stir continually until mixture thickens.
8. Pour two-thirds of the curry sauce over tuna and rice. Mix.
9. Spoon into a casserole, pour the remaining sauce over the top.
10. Cover with breadcrumbs and bake in a preheated oven until golden and heated through (about 30 minutes).

To store: cover and refrigerate for 24 hours.

Nutritional data per serve: 1527 kJ (365 cal), CHO 45 g, Protein 36 g, Fat 4 g.

Preparation time: 1 hour 40 minutes. Cooking equipment: 2 saucepans, casserole. Oven temperature: 160 °C (325 °F, gas 3).

Salmon Mornay

Serves 4

440 g (15 oz) canned
   salmon
4 spring onions (shallots),
   chopped
75 ml (2 ½ fl oz) lemon
   juice
2 celery sticks, finely
   chopped
40 ml (8 tsp) freshly
   grated Parmesan cheese
1 quantity Cheese Sauce
   (page 152)
garnish: 2 hard-boiled
   eggs, chopped

Method:

1. Mix salmon, spring onions (shallots), lemon juice and celery in a casserole.
2. Add Parmesan cheese to sauce and pour over salmon mixture. Mix well.
3. Bake in a preheated oven for 30 minutes. Alternatively, cover and microwave on Medium for 12 – 14 minutes. Leave to stand, covered, for 5 minutes before serving.
4. Sprinkle with chopped eggs and serve.

Nutritional data per serve: 1219 kJ (291 cal), CHO 12 g, Protein 32 g, Fat 13 g.

Preparation time: 45 minutes. Cooking equipment: mornay dish or shallow casserole. Oven temperature: 180 °C (350 °F, gas 4).

Seafood Pasta

Serves 4

300 g (10 oz) pasta
   (spaghetti, tagliatelle
   or macaroni)
40 ml (8 tsp) water
½ medium onion,
   chopped
1 clove garlic, crushed
250 ml (8 fl oz, 1 cup)
   skimmed milk
10 ml (2 tsp) cornflour
   (cornstarch)
170 g (6 oz, 1½ cups)
   mixed cooked seafood
   (oysters, prawns,
   shrimps, clams,
   scallops)
20 ml (4 tsp) chopped
   parsley
coarsely ground black
   pepper to taste
salt to taste

Method:

1. Fill a large saucepan to two-thirds with water and bring to a rapid boil. Add pasta, and boil rapidly for 10 – 12 minutes until *al dente* (tender, but still firm to the bite).

2. While the pasta is cooking, prepare the sauce. In a medium saucepan, boil the 40 ml (8 tsp) water. Add the onion and garlic and cook until tender.

3. In a small bowl, blend 20 ml (4 tsp) of the milk with the cornflour (cornstarch) to make a smooth paste. Then stir in the remaining milk. Add mixture to the onion and garlic, and stir constantly over medium heat until sauce thickens.

4. Over medium heat, add all remaining ingredients, and stir to combine and heat through.

5. Drain the pasta and add to sauce. Toss gently to combine.

6. Serve at once.

Nutritional data per serve: 1495 kJ (357 cal), CHO 48 g, Protein 31 g, Fat 4 g.

Preparation time: 30 minutes. Cooking equipment: large saucepan, medium saucepan.

Whole Fish in Ginger

Serves 4

1 x 1 kg (2 lb) whole fish,
   gutted and scaled but
   with head intact
10 ml (2 tsp) chopped
   fresh ginger
1 clove garlic, crushed
60 ml (2 fl oz, ¼ cup) soy
   sauce
juice of 1 lemon

Method:

1. Using a very sharp knife, score the skin of the fish on each side, three or four times, at equal intervals and at an angle to the backbone.

2. Place fish on its side in a flat dish, or support it upright with wooden skewers.

3. Combine remaining ingredients to make a marinade and pour over the fish.

4. Bake the fish, uncovered, in a preheated oven for 30 minutes or until fish flakes when tested with a fork. Baste frequently with the marinade during cooking.

175 ml (6 fl oz, ¾ cup)
dry white wine
4 spring onions
(shallots), sliced
lengthways
garnish: thin slices of
lemon

5. Serve the fish whole with cooking juices, garnished with lemon slices. Accompany with boiled brown rice and a green salad.

Microwave: at step 4, cover with cling film (plastic wrap) and cook on High for 15 minutes.

Nutritional data per serve: 497 kJ (119 cal), CHO 1 g, Protein 22 g, Fat 3 g.

Preparation time: 40 minutes. Cooking equipment: shallow casserole. Oven temperature: 180 °C (350 °F, gas 4).

Vegetable-Stuffed Trout

Serves 4

4 small trout, gutted
juice of 2 lemons
40 ml (8 tsp) mixed fresh
herbs, chopped (such
as thyme, parsley,
marjoram)
4 spring onions
(shallots), finely
chopped
20 ml (4 tsp) finely
chopped celery
40 ml (8 tsp) finely
chopped green pepper
(capsicum)
4 mushrooms, finely
chopped
5 ml (1 tsp) ground black
pepper

Serve the trout with plenty of noodles, rice or potatoes, plus a salad, and you have a well-rounded main course.

Method:
1. Wash fish.
2. Place each fish on a piece of foil large enough to wrap it up completely.
3. Pour lemon juice over the outside and inside of fish.
4. Combine all other ingredients in a mixing bowl.
5. Divide into four and pack a quarter of the mixture into the cavity of each fish.
6. Wrap firmly in foil. Seal edges carefully.
7. Bake in a preheated oven or cook under a grill until cooked through (about 10 – 15 minutes).

Microwave: follow the same method as above except use a suitable large shallow microwave dish and secure the cavity of each fish with cocktail sticks (toothpicks). Cover dish with clingfilm (plastic wrap). Bake on Medium-high for 8 – 12 minutes. Leave to stand, covered, for 5 minutes before serving.

Nutritional data per serve: 511 kJ (122 cal), CHO 1 g, Protein 23 g, Fat 3 g.

Preparation time: 20 minutes. Cooking equipment: baking dish. Oven temperature: 180 °C (350 °F, gas 4), or use grill.

Pasta and Smoked Trout

Serves 4

250 g (8 oz) fettucine

1 medium smoked trout

125 ml (4 fl oz, ½ cup)
  dry white wine

2.5 ml (½ tsp) garlic
  granules (or 1 clove,
  chopped)

2.5 ml (½ tsp) mustard
  powder

½ quantity White Sauce
  (page 151)

garnish: chopped capers

Method:

1. Boil fettucine in water as directed on the pack; drain.
2. While pasta is cooking, skin the trout and remove the flesh from the bones by lifting it off with a fork. Break the flesh into bite-sized pieces.
3. Mix wine, garlic and mustard and bring to the boil in large saucepan. Add the White Sauce and reheat gently.
4. Add the fettucine and mix through, reheating gently.
5. Add the fish, mixing carefully. When the fish is hot, turn it on to a serving dish and sprinkle with chopped capers.

Nutritional data per serve: 1490 kJ (356 cal), CHO 48 g, Protein 28 g, Fat 5 g.

Preparation time: 30 – 35 minutes, including time for preparing White Sauce. Cooking equipment: 2 large saucepans.

Crab Quiche

Serves 4

1 quantity Wholemeal
  Pastry (page 186)

170 g (6 oz) canned crab
  meat

1 courgette (zucchini,
  baby marrow), sliced

2 spring onions
  (shallots), chopped

60 g (2 oz, ¼ cup) ricotta
  cheese

4 eggs

250 ml (8 fl oz, 1 cup)
  skimmed milk

250 ml (8 fl oz, 1 cup)
  low-fat plain yoghurt

pepper to taste

good pinch of salt
  (optional)

You can make this quiche just as successfully with shrimps instead of crab, or fresh seafood instead of canned. Asparagus or mushrooms make delicious substitutes for the courgette (zucchini, baby marrow).

Method:

1. Roll out pastry and line flan dish.
2. Place crab meat, sliced courgette (zucchini, baby marrow) and spring onions (shallots) over base of pastry.
3. Blend all other ingredients and pour over filling.
4. Bake in a preheated oven for 30 – 45 minutes or until filling is set.

To store: cover and refrigerate for up to 2 days. Do not reheat or the filling will toughen.

Nutritional data per serve: 2737 kJ (654 cal), CHO 56 g, Protein 30 g, Fat 34 g.

Preparation time: 45 – 60 minutes. Cooking equipment: flan dish. Oven temperature: 180 °C (350 °F, gas 4).

Paella

Serves 8

---

10 ml (2 tsp) olive oil

8 small chicken pieces
(not wings), skin
removed

pinch each of salt and
black pepper

1 large onion, chopped

2 large tomatoes, chopped

5 ml (1 tsp) chopped,
crushed or minced
garlic

good pinch of saffron
powder

410 g (14 oz, 2 cups) long-
grain brown rice

450 ml (¾ pint, 2 cups)
water

1 chicken stock cube

1 small green or red
pepper (capsicum), cut
into strips

150 g (5 oz, 1 cup) frozen
peas

12 cooked king prawns,
heads removed, shelled
and cleaned (with tails
left on)

This is a wonderful dinner party or luncheon dish, served with a green salad and crusty wholemeal bread.

Method:

1. Heat oil in frying pan.
2. Sprinkle chicken pieces lightly with black pepper and a pinch of salt (if desired).
3. Add to frying pan and brown well on all sides. Remove from the frying pan and set aside on a plate.
4. Add onion to pan and brown.
5. Add tomato and garlic, cook until soft.
6. Add saffron and rice. Stir.
7. Pour in water and stock cube; mix well.
8. Spoon into casserole.
9. Stir pepper (capsicum) strips, peas and chicken pieces into mixture.
10. Cover and cook in a preheated oven until rice is cooked through and liquid absorbed (about 1 hour).
11. Just before serving, add the prawns and allow to heat through. Serve immediately from the casserole.

Nutritional data per serve: 1312 kJ (313 cal), CHO 41 g, Protein 24 g, Fat 5 g.

Preparation time: 2 – 3 hours. Cooking equipment: frying pan, large shallow casserole. Oven temperature: 200 °C (400 °F, gas 6).

Mussels à la Grecque

Serves 4

---

10 ml (2 tsp) olive oil

2 medium leeks, sliced

3 large tomatoes, peeled, or 410 g (14 oz) canned tomatoes, chopped

20 ml (4 tsp) tomato paste

good pinch of dried basil

2.5 ml (½ tsp) dried oregano

ground black pepper to taste

salt to taste (not needed if you use canned tomatoes)

1.5 kg (3 lb) mussels in shells, scrubbed and beards removed

Black mussels are ideal for this recipe. However, it's also excellent with clams. Green-lipped mussels or periwinkles are also perfect for cooking this way.

Method:

1. Heat oil in a saucepan and sauté leeks until tender.
2. Add tomatoes, tomato paste, basil, oregano, pepper and salt, if using.
3. Bring to the boil and add mussels.
4. Cover and cook until shells open (this takes only a few minutes). Discard any mussels that do not open.
5. Serve in bowls with crusty bread.

Nutritional data per serve: 723 kJ (173 cal), CHO 6 g, Protein 25 g, Fat 5 g.

Preparation time: 15 – 20 minutes. Cooking equipment: large saucepan.

Foreground: Chick-Pea Savoury. On the round platter, left, assorted pumpernickel savouries, right Vegetable Samosas, Salmon and Ricotta Loaf in the centre, and Dolmades at the back.

Seafood Cannelloni

Serves 4

10 ml (2 tsp) olive oil

2 garlic cloves, crushed

2 medium onions, finely
  chopped

125 ml (4 fl oz, ½ cup)
  tomato paste

450 ml (¾ pint, 2 cups)
  water

10 ml (2 tsp) lemon juice

2.5 ml (½ tsp) dried
  thyme

5 ml (1 tsp) dried basil

salt to taste (optional)

200 g (7 oz) white fish,
  cut into small chunks

150 g (5 oz) shelled
  prawns, coarsely
  chopped

100 g (3½ oz) scallops,
  coarsely chopped

30 g (1 oz, ½ cup) fresh
  wholemeal breadcrumbs

40 ml (8 tsp) chopped
  parsley

40 ml (8 tsp) dry white
  wine

ground black pepper

1 egg, lightly beaten

12 lightly cooked
  cannelloni shells

60 g (2 oz, ½ cup) grated
  low-fat hard cheese

This is a recipe for special occasions. For a family meal you may like to omit the scallops and prawns and replace them with 500 g (1 lb) of minced white fish.

Method:

1. Heat oil in frying pan and sauté 1 garlic clove and 1 onion until tender.
2. Add tomato paste, water, lemon juice, good pinch of thyme, 2.5 ml (1/2 tsp) basil and salt (if using). Set aside.
3. Combine remaining thyme and basil with fish, prawns, scallops, breadcrumbs, parsley, wine, pepper and egg.
4. Spoon fish mixture into cannelloni shells and arrange in a shallow casserole.
5. Pour tomato mixture over cannelloni shells and sprinkle with cheese.
6. Bake in a preheated oven for 30 minutes until sauce is hot and bubbling.

Nutritional data per serve: 1747 kJ (417 cal), CHO 40 g, Protein 38 g, Fat 11 g.

Preparation time: 1 hour. Cooking equipment: frying pan, shallow casserole. Oven temperature: 180 °C (350 °F, gas 4).

Crêpes with fillings: foreground Steak and Onion, centre Ham and Asparagus, delicious Flambéed Fruit at the top.

Meat and Poultry

Pork Tango

Serves 4

250 ml (8 fl oz, 1 cup)
  boiling water
60 g (4 oz, ½ cup)
  chopped dried apricots
20 ml (4 tsp) currants
500 g (1 lb) pork fillet,
  trimmed of fat
1 beaten egg
10 ml (2 tsp) sesame
  seeds
40 ml (8 tsp) fresh
  breadcrumbs
1 garlic clove, finely
  chopped or minced
  (optional)
40 ml (8 tsp) mango
  chutney or Fresh
  Mango Pickle
  (page 161)
20 ml (4 tsp) brandy
60 ml (2 fl oz, ¼ cup)
  canned evaporated
  skimmed milk

This is a favourite recipe. The alcohol in the brandy evaporates during cooking but rounds out the lovely fruity sauce. Leave it out if you prefer. You can substitute 125 g (4 oz, 1/2 cup) crushed pineapple for the apricots, but remember to reduce the water to 125 ml (4 fl oz, 1/2 cup).

Method:

1. Pour boiling water over apricots and currants in a bowl and leave to stand for 30 minutes.
2. Roll pork first in egg and then in a mixture of sesame seeds, breadcrumbs and garlic until well coated.
3. Place in roasting pan and bake, uncovered, in a preheated oven for 45 minutes.
4. While meat is cooking, heat apricots in a saucepan with the currants and the water in which they were soaked.
5. Simmer gently until water is almost absorbed.
6. Add chutney and brandy and stir until the sauce returns to the simmer.
7. Pour evaporated skimmed milk into a heat-resistant bowl and gradually stir in the hot apricot mixture (this method will prevent the milk from curdling).
8. Return to saucepan and reheat without boiling.
9. To test if meat is cooked, pierce with a skewer. The juice should be clear.
10. Cut meat into eight slices, arrange two slices on each serving plate and spoon sauce over, distributing apricot halves evenly.

To store: both meat and sauce will keep for two days if well covered in the refrigerator. They can be served cold, in which case store meat in one piece and slice thinly just before serving, using the cold sauce as an accompaniment.

Nutritional data per serve: 1057 kJ (252 cal), CHO 22 g, Protein 34 g, Fat 4 g.

Preparation time: 1 hour. Cooking equipment: roasting pan, small saucepan, heat-proof bowl. Oven temperature: 200 °C (400 °F, gas 6).

Stir-Fried Pork

Serves 4 – 5

500 g (1 lb) pork fillet
20 ml (4 tsp) oil
2.5 ml (½ tsp) fresh
   ginger, grated
1 clove garlic, crushed
pinch of Chinese five-
   spice powder
150 g (5 oz, 1 cup) small
   broccoli florets
150 g (5 oz, 1 cup) small
   cauliflower florets
½ green pepper
   (capsicum), diced
2 medium carrots, cut
   into matchsticks
   (julienne)
3 spring onions
   (shallots), chopped
16 – 20 mangetout
   (snow peas)
10 – 12 button
   mushrooms, sliced
2 celery sticks, sliced
   diagonally
1 apple, cut into slices
¼ cucumber, cut into
   slices
20 ml (4 tsp) soy sauce
20 ml (4 tsp) clear honey
20 ml (4 tsp) tomato
   sauce
30 ml (6 tsp) cornflour
   (cornstarch)
250 ml (8 fl oz, 1 cup)
   Chicken Stock (page 72)

The secret of a successful stir-fry is to have all the ingredients prepared before you begin cooking, and then to cook them swiftly so that they reach the table still crisp and alive with colour.

Method:

1. Prepare pork fillet by slicing thinly at an angle.
2. Heat oil in large pan or wok until very hot. Add pork, ginger, garlic and five-spice. Stir-fry for 3 – 5 minutes.
3. Add broccoli, cauliflower, pepper (capsicum) and carrots. Stir-fry for 1 – 2 minutes, making sure that nothing is allowed to over-cook and become limp.
4. Now add the rest of the vegetables and continue stir-frying over high heat for another 1 – 2 minutes.
5. In a bowl, combine soy sauce, honey, tomato sauce, cornflour (cornstarch) and chicken stock. Add mixture to the chicken and vegetables, bring to the boil, cover, turn down the heat and simmer for 2 – 3 minutes only.
6. Serve on a bed of boiled brown rice.

To vary: replace the pork with chicken or veal.

Nutritional data per serve (based on 4 serves): 1329 kJ (318 cal), CHO 25 g, Protein 31 g, Fat 11 g.

Preparation time: 45 minutes. Cooking equipment: large saucepan or wok.

Meat Loaf with Spicy Barbecue Sauce

Serves 4

500 g (1 lb) minced lean
  beef
3 slices of wholemeal
  bread, crumbed
1 onion, finely chopped
10 ml (2 tsp) Curry
  Powder (page 162)
20 ml (4 tsp) chopped
  parsley
1 egg
125 ml (4 fl oz, ½ cup)
  skimmed or low-fat
  milk
Sauce:
125 ml (4 fl oz, ½ cup)
  water
125 ml (4 fl oz, ½ cup)
  tomato sauce
60 ml (2 fl oz, ¼ cup)
  Worcestershire sauce
40 ml (8 tsp) wine
  vinegar
5 ml (1 tsp) instant coffee
  powder
juice of 1 lemon
20 ml (4 tsp) cornflour
  (cornstarch)
20 ml (4 tsp) water

This meat loaf cooks in its own luscious, dark, piquant sauce.

Method:

1. Combine minced beef, breadcrumbs, onion, Curry Powder, parsley and egg.
2. Stir until mixture is well combined.
3. Add milk and continue stirring until mixture is smooth.
4. Shape meat mixture into a loaf and place in baking dish.
5. Bake in a preheated oven for 30 minutes, or microwave, covered, on Medium for 20 minutes.
6. Remove from oven or microwave and drain off any fat.
7. In a saucepan, combine all sauce ingredients, except the cornflour (cornstarch) and 20 ml (4 tsp) of water, bring slowly to the boil, reduce heat and simmer for 5 minutes.
8. Pour sauce over meat and return to oven or microwave.
9. Bake for a further 20 – 30 minutes, basting frequently with sauce, or microwave on Medium for a further 20 minutes.
10. Mix cornflour (cornstarch) and water to a smooth paste. Remove meat loaf to a serving plate and slice.
11. Add cornflour (cornstarch) mixture to the sauce in the baking dish and bring back to the boil, stirring constantly until thickened.
12. Pour thickened sauce over the meat loaf. Serve hot with vegetables or cold with salad.

To store: keep in airtight container or cover with clingfilm (plastic wrap) in refrigerator for up to two days. You can also freeze it in an airtight container.

Nutritional data per serve: 1210 kJ (289 cal), CHO 24 g, Protein 34 g, Fat 7 g.

Preparation time: 1 hour. Cooking equipment: baking dish, medium saucepan. Oven temperature: 180 °C (350 °F, gas 4).

Meatballs in Tomato Sauce

Serves 4

500 g (1 lb) lean minced
   beef
20 ml (4 tsp) chopped
   parsley
5 ml (1 tsp) Curry
   Powder (page 162)
3 slices of wholemeal
   bread, crumbed
1 beaten egg
10 ml (2 tsp) water
2 medium onions, finely
   chopped
410 g (14 oz) canned
   tomatoes
20 ml (4 tsp) tomato
   paste
2.5 ml (½ tsp) dried
   oregano
ground black pepper to
   taste
garnish: parsley

All you need do is to make the meatballs, prepare potatoes, brown rice, crushed wheat or noodles, make a mixed salad, and you have a perfect meal.

Method:

1. Combine beef, parsley, Curry Powder and breadcrumbs in a bowl.
2. Add the egg and water to bind the mixture.
3. Roll into sixteen equal balls.
4. Place in a baking dish and cook in a preheated oven at 180 °C (350 °F, gas 4) for 30 minutes.
6. Heat saucepan with 10 ml (2 tsp) of water and cook the onion lightly until translucent, stirring frequently.
6. Add tomatoes, tomato paste and oregano.
7. Reduce heat and simmer for 10 minutes.
8. Add pepper to taste.
9. Pour sauce over meatballs, replace in oven and reduce heat to 160 °C (325 °F, gas 3).
10. Bake for a further 30 minutes.
11. Serve, garnished with parsley.

To store: cover and refrigerate for up to three days.

Microwave: follow Steps 1 to 3 above, then preheat a browning dish on High for 6 – 7 minutes. Place the meatballs on the browning dish and cook them on High for 4 – 6 minutes, turning the meatballs three times during the cooking process. Remove the meatballs to a shallow microwave dish and set aside. Place the onions in a bowl and cook them on High until they are translucent. Add the tomatoes, tomato paste and oregano to the onions. Cook the onion mixture on High for 5 minutes. Add pepper to taste. Pour the sauce over the meatballs and cook on Medium for a further 15 minutes.

Nutritional data per serve: 1016 kJ (243 cal), CHO 13 g, Protein 33 g, Fat 7 g.
Preparation time: 1½ hours. Cooking equipment: baking dish, saucepan.
Oven temperature: 180 °C (350 °F, gas 4), then 160 °C (325 °F, gas 3).

Beef Curry

Serves 4

*500 g (1 lb) lean beef
ground black pepper
10 ml (2 tsp) oil (optional)
1 large onion peeled and
 chopped
2 potatoes, scrubbed and
 chopped
125 g (4 oz, ½ cup)
 pumpkin, skinned and
 chopped
125 g (4 oz, ½ cup) sweet
 potato (yam), peeled
 and chopped
2 courgettes (zucchini)
 cut into chunks
5 ml (1 tsp) dried
 coriander
5 ml (1 tsp) dried cumin
2.5 ml (½ tsp) dried
 cardamom seeds
10 ml (2 tsp) mustard
 seeds
2.5 – 5 ml (½ – 1 tsp)
 dried ground chillies
10 ml (2 tsp) finely
 chopped or minced
 fresh ginger
10 ml (2 tsp) finely
 chopped or minced
 garlic
250 ml (8 fl oz, 1 cup)
 water
pinch of salt to taste
 (optional)*

This dish is best when prepared the day before eating, to allow the flavour to develop. A pinch of salt helps to bring out the flavour of the spices, but use discretion.

Method:

1. Trim any fat from meat. Cut into 2.5 cm (1 inch) cubes and sprinkle with pepper.
2. In a frying pan, dry-fry (or sauté in 10 ml (2 tsp) of hot oil) until browned on all sides. Set aside in a bowl.
3. In the same frying pan, sauté the vegetables and set aside with the meat.
4. Now add the spices to the frying pan and cook for 3 – 4 minutes over medium heat to release the fragrance, then add the ginger and garlic.
5. Add water and stir the pan juices well.
6. Return meat and vegetables to pan, add salt if desired, and stir to combine the flavours.
7. Spoon into casserole, cover and cook in a preheated oven for about 1½ – 2 hours until meat is tender.
8. Serve with brown rice and the accompaniments suggested below.

To store: cover and refrigerate for up to four days.

***Nutritional data per serve: 1169 kJ (279 cal), CHO 18 g,
Protein 31 g, Fat 9 g.***

*Preparation time: 2½ hours. Cooking equipment: large frying pan,
casserole. Oven temperature: 200 °C (400 °F, gas 6).*

Curry Accompaniments

Fresh Mango Pickle (page 161), pineapple slices, sultanas with coconut and diced apple are all excellent with curry.

Tomato Mint Salad	Mix 1 ripe tomato, finely chopped, with 2 spring onions (shallots), sliced, and 10 ml (2 tsp) chopped fresh mint. Chill until ready to serve.
	Nutritional data per serve: 36 kJ (9 cal), CHO 2 g, Protein 1 g, Fat 0 g.
Banana-Yoghurt Relish	Slice 2 firm bananas and sprinkle them with 20 ml (4 tsp) shredded coconut. Spoon 60 ml (2 fl oz, 1/4 cup) low-fat plain yoghurt over bananas and combine. Chill until ready to serve.
	Nutritional data per serve: 389 kJ (93 cal), CHO 17 g, Protein 2 g, Fat 2 g.
Cucumber and Yoghurt	Slice a piece of cucumber about 10 cm (4 inches) long and combine with 10 ml (2 tsp) lemon juice and 2.5 ml (1/2 tsp) mustard seeds. Spoon 60 ml (2 fl oz, 1/4 cup) of low-fat plain yoghurt over the cucumber and combine with yoghurt. Chill until ready to serve.
	Nutritional data per serve: 46 kJ (11 cal), CHO 1 g, Protein 1 g, Fat 0 g.

Baked Fillet with Cherry Sauce

Serves 8

1 kg (2 lb) fillet of beef, trimmed of visible fat

10 ml (2 tsp) chopped fresh oregano or 5 ml (1 tsp) dried

3 small sprigs fresh rosemary or 5 ml (1 tsp) dried

1 quantity Cherry Sauce (page 155)

garnish: oregano or rosemary sprigs

Fillet of beef is an expensive cut but for a special occasion it is worth it. Remember, too, that there is no waste and, in this recipe, you can serve eight with only 1 kg (2 lb) of fillet.

Method:

1. Place the beef on a large piece of foil.
2. Sprinkle with oregano and rosemary and wrap beef.
3. Place in a baking dish; bake in a preheated oven for 30 minutes.
4. Uncover and bake for a further 15 minutes.
5. Remove from oven, pour juices into Cherry Sauce. Cover meat loosely with foil and leave to stand in a warm place.
6. Heat sauce.
7. Cut beef into thick slices and serve topped with Cherry Sauce and garnished with sprigs of oregano or rosemary.

Nutritional data per serve: 728 kJ (174 cal), CHO 6 g, Protein 27 g, Fat 5 g.

Preparation time: approximately 1 hour. Cooking equipment: baking dish.

Oven temperature: 220 °C (425 °F, gas 7).

Pickled Beef

Serves 8

1 x 1 kg (2 lb) piece topside of beef
12 whole cloves
250 ml (8 fl oz, 1 cup) wine vinegar (red or white)
250 ml (8 fl oz, 1 cup) red wine
10 ml (2 tsp) soft brown sugar
2.5 ml (½ tsp) prepared mustard
2.5 ml (½ tsp) mustard seeds
2.5 ml (½ tsp) finely chopped garlic
2.5 ml (½ tsp) peppercorns
1 medium onion, chopped

You may never have considered making your own pickled beef, so this delicious recipe may be an eye-opener. The commercial product tends to be full of salt and saltpetre which is not desirable.

Method:
1. Trim any fat from meat.
2. Stick cloves into meat, evenly distributed.
3. Place meat in a bowl large enough to hold it snugly.
4. Combine vinegar, wine, sugar, mustard, mustard seeds, garlic, peppercorns and onions and pour over meat.
5. Cover tightly and refrigerate for three days, turning once or twice each day.
6. Remove meat from bowl and place in a large saucepan.
7. Strain marinating liquid through a sieve into a smaller saucepan. Bring to the boil and strain over meat.
8. Cover, bring to the boil, lower the heat immediately, and simmer gently until meat is cooked through (about 1 hour).
9. Serve hot with boiled or mashed potatoes and cooked red cabbage, or cold with bread or with a salad.

To store: cover and refrigerate for up to one week. Excellent to take camping.

Nutritional data per serve: 658 kJ (157 cal), CHO 2 g, Protein 27 g, Fat 5 g.
Preparation time: 1½ hours plus 3 days marinating. Cooking equipment: saucepan, large saucepan with lid.

Chilli Con Carne

Serves 4

500 g (1 lb) topside of beef, cubed
10 ml (2 tsp) oil (optional)
1 large onion, chopped
4 large tomatoes, chopped

This dish is equally successful if you use lean beef mince instead of topside.

Method:
1. Trim off all fat from topside and cut into 2.5 cm (1 inch) cubes.
2. Brush frying pan with oil and brown meat or dry-fry meat until well browned.

150 g (5 oz) canned
   tomato paste
250 ml (8 fl oz, 1 cup)
   water and 60 ml
   (2 fl oz, ¼ cup) water
410 g (14 oz) canned red
   kidney beans
10 ml (2 tsp) Tabasco
good pinch of ground
   black pepper
20 ml (4 tsp) cornflour
   (cornstarch)

3. Spoon into casserole.
4. Add onion to frying pan and sauté until lightly browned.
5. Add tomatoes and cook over medium heat until soft. Stir occasionally.
6. Stir in tomato paste and 250 ml (8 fl oz, 1 cup) water. Mix well.
7. Rinse kidney beans, drain well, and add to the mixture.
8. Add Tabasco and pepper, pour over meat and combine.
9. Mix cornflour (cornstarch) with 60 ml (2 fl oz, 1/4 cup) water. When smooth, stir into mixture.
10. Cover casserole and cook in a preheated oven until meat is tender (about 1 1/2 hours).

To store: cover and refrigerate for up to three days.

Nutritional data per serve: 1485 kJ (355 cal), CHO 34 g, Protein 39 g, Fat 7 g.

Preparation time: 2 hours. Cooking equipment: large frying pan or electric frying pan, lidded casserole. Oven temperature: 180 °C (350 °F, gas 4).

Steak and Black Bean Sauce

Serves 4

10 ml (2 tsp) oil
500 g (1 lb) fillet or lean
   rump steak, trimmed
   of fat
1 medium onion, peeled
   and quartered
45 g (1 ½ oz, ¼ cup)
   coarsely chopped green
   pepper (capsicum)
45 g (1 ½ oz, ¼ cup)
   coarsely chopped red
   pepper (capsicum)
1 medium carrot, sliced
1 quantity Black Bean
   Sauce (page 154)

None of the ingredients in this recipe should be cooked for more than a few minutes. At the table, the vegetables should still be crisp and have their true vibrant colour.

Method:
1. Brush oil over the base of a frying pan or wok and heat over high heat.
2. Slice steak into very thin strips 3 – 4 cm (1 1/4 – 1 1/2 inches) long. Sauté quickly for about 3 minutes.
3. Add vegetables and stir-fry for a further 2 minutes.
4. Add Black Bean Sauce, cover and simmer gently for 5 minutes.
5. Serve with boiled brown rice.

Nutritional data per serve: 1031 kJ (246 cal), CHO 6 g, Protein 32 g, Fat 11 g.

Preparation time: ½ hour. Cooking equipment: frying pan or wok.

Beef à la Pizzaiola

Serves 4

500 g (1 lb) lean fillet of
   beef
5 ml (1 tsp) oil
1 clove garlic, crushed
45 g (½ oz, ½ cup) sliced
   mushrooms
2 large tomatoes, peeled
   and chopped
2 spring onions
   (shallots), chopped
4 leaves fresh basil,
   roughly chopped, or
   good pinch of dried
   basil
freshly ground black
   pepper
salt to taste (optional)

Although beef fillet is a relatively expensive cut of meat, in this recipe you use only 500 g (1 lb) to feed four people. The meat cooks quickly, so there is little shrinkage and, as fillet is lean, there is no waste. The recipe will work just as successfully if you use veal, pork or chicken. Add a few drops of Tabasco if you want to make the sauce more piquant.

Method:

1. Cut the meat into thin strips, about 12 mm (1/2 inch) wide and 5 cm (2 inches) long.
2. Brush oil over the base of a heavy frying pan and heat the pan over medium-high heat.
3. When hot, toss in the meat and stir-fry until well sealed and browned (about 2 – 3 minutes).
4. Set the meat aside on a warm plate and continue as follows. To the hot frying pan add the garlic and the mushrooms and stir-fry for a further few seconds until the mushrooms are lightly cooked.
5. Add the tomatoes, spring onions (shallots), basil, pepper and salt, and bring to a simmer. Now return the meat to the sauce and simmer for about 5 minutes, or until the meat is cooked and the dish is hot.
6. Finally, spoon the meat and sauce on to a bed of rice or noodles, garnish with spring onions (shallots) and serve.

To store: cover and refrigerate for up to three days.

Nutritional data per serve: 713 kJ (170 cal), CHO 3 g, Protein 28 g, Fat 5 g.
Preparation time: 15 minutes. Cooking equipment: large saucepan, large frying pan.

Leg of Lamb with Garlic and Mustard

Serves 8

1.5 kg (3 lb) leg of lamb
2 cloves garlic, crushed
5 ml (1 tsp) dried
   rosemary
40 ml (8 tsp) soy sauce
60 ml (2 fl oz) French
   mustard
40 ml (8 tsp) cornflour
   (cornstarch)
250 ml (8 fl oz, 1 cup)
   water
garnish: rosemary or
   mint sprig

Method:
1. Trim all fat from the lamb; place the lamb in a baking dish.
2. Combine garlic, rosemary, soy sauce and mustard and spread over leg of lamb.
3. Bake, covered, in a preheated oven until cooked to your taste.
4. Remove leg of lamb from dish and carve.
5. Pour or skim the fat from meat juices.
6. Blend cornflour (cornstarch) with a little water to form a smooth paste and add to the meat juices.
7. Heat until thickened, stirring constantly to keep the gravy smooth, and pour over slices of lamb.

To store: cover and refrigerate for up to three days.

Nutritional data per serve: 671 kJ (160 cal), CHO 2 g, Protein 27 g, Fat 5 g.

Preparation time: 1¾ – 2 hours. Cooking equipment: baking dish.
Oven temperature: 180 °C (350 °F, gas 4).

Skewered Lamb

Serves 4
(3 skewers each)

250 ml (8 fl oz, 1 cup)
   low-fat plain yoghurt
60 ml (2 fl oz) French
   mustard
good pinch of dried
   thyme
good pinch of dried
   oregano
2 rosemary sprigs
2 bay leaves
500 g (1 lb) lean lamb,
   diced

Baked jacket potatoes and a large mixed salad make this a memorable meal.

Method:
1. Mix yoghurt with mustard and herbs, add lamb and stir well.
2. Leave to marinate for 10 – 12 hours.
3. Remove rosemary and bay leaves.
4. Thread meat on to skewers, grill or barbecue until cooked.

Nutritional data per serve: 744 kJ (178 cal), CHO 3 g, Protein 30 g, Fat 5 g.

Preparation time: 1 hour, plus 10 – 12 hours marinating time.
Cooking equipment: 12 wooden skewers (soaked in water for 1 hour before using to prevent burning), grill or barbecue.

Veal Mango

Serves 4

Sauce:

2 small or 1 large mango

250 ml (8 fl oz, 1 cup) dry white wine

60 ml (2 fl oz) mango chutney or Fresh Mango Pickle (page 161)

30 g (1 oz) spring onions (shallots), chopped

Veal:

5 ml (1 tsp) oil

4 lean veal schnitzels

40 ml (8 tsp) water

garnish: spring onions (shallots)

This is a wonderful recipe that is very easy to prepare and yet looks and tastes good enough for a special occasion. Simple boiled rice and a crisp green salad complete the meal. Pork schnitzel or chicken fillets make an excellent and economical substitute for the veal.

Method:

1. Make the sauce. Peel the mango. Cut away and roughly slice the flesh.
2. Place the mango flesh in a saucepan. Add the white wine and pickle or chutney. Bring to the boil, reduce heat and simmer until the sauce has reduced by half, about 15 minutes.
3. If you want a smooth sauce, purée the hot fruit mixture in a food processor or blender, or press through a sieve. Return to saucepan.
4. Add the chopped spring onions (shallots). Return to the boil, reduce heat and simmer for a further 2 – 3 minutes.
5. Prepare the veal schnitzels. While the sauce is simmering, (Step 2), brush a large frying pan with the oil and heat over medium-high heat.
6. Fry the schnitzels, turning occasionally, for about 10 minutes until browned on both sides.
7. Remove the cooked schnitzels from the pan. Add the 40 ml (8 tsp) of water to the pan; add the sauce. Heat, stirring constantly, for about 3 minutes.
8. Arrange the schnitzels on individual plates. Spoon over the sauce and garnish with whole spring onions (shallots).

Nutritional data per serve: 734 kJ (175 cal), CHO 9 g, Protein 28 g, Fat 3 g.

Preparation time: 40 minutes. Cooking equipment: saucepan, frying pan.

Opposite: Foreground left: fresh lychees, Beef and Black Bean Sauce at the right, Gado Gado served with Chicken and Saté Sauce at centre, and a steamer of brown rice with Hot and Sour Soup below.

Overleaf:
Front right: Chicken Enchiladas, a Tossed Salad at centre with Mexicale Pie with Corn Dumplings beside it, and a cool Golden Fruit Flummery at the top.

Caesar's Chicken

Serves 4

1 x 800 g (1¾ lb) chicken

350 ml (12 fl oz, 1½ cups) water

2 – 3 fresh dill sprigs or good pinch of dried dill

60 ml (2 fl oz, ¼ cup) vinegar

1 small leek, sliced

Sauce:

200 g (7 oz) dates, pitted

1 chicken stock cube

5 ml (1 tsp) caraway seeds

2.5 ml (½ tsp) ground coriander

good pinch of ground cardamom

10 ml (2 tsp) chopped fresh mint

2.5 ml (½ tsp) minced fresh ginger

10 ml (2 tsp) Plum Sauce (page 161)

60 ml (2 fl oz) wine vinegar

250 ml (8 fl oz, 1 cup) water

The touch of sweetness and the thickness of the sauce in this Middle Eastern dish come from the addition of dates.

Method:

1. Cut chicken into pieces, discarding wings, skin and fat.
2. Place chicken in saucepan with water, dill, vinegar and leek.
3. Cover, bring to the boil, immediately turn down the heat and simmer gently for 30 minutes.
4. Chop dates and place in second saucepan. Add stock cube, caraway, coriander, cardamom, mint, ginger, plum sauce, vinegar and water.
5. Cook, stirring gently, until the dates have broken down and the sauce thickens.
6. Lift chicken out of cooking broth, place in casserole or baking dish, pour sauce over, cover with foil and bake in a preheated oven for 15 – 20 minutes.

To store: cover and refrigerate for up to two days.

Nutritional data per serve: 1306 kJ (312 cal), CHO 33 g, Protein 32 g, Fat 6 g.

Preparation time: 1 hour. Cooking equipment: 2 saucepans, shallow open baking dish or casserole.

Oven temperature: 180 °C (350 °F, gas 4).

Previous page:
Foreground: Vegetable-Stuffed Trout, centre right a platter of Skewered Lamb and Vegetables en Brochette beside a basket of wholemeal damper. At the top Coleslaw, Curried Sweet Potato and Banana Salad and Broccoli, Beanshoots and Mangetout (Snow Peas) with Lemon.

Opposite:
Foreground: Aubergine (Eggplant) Neapolitan, centre Spiced Oranges with Creamy Whipped Topping, to the left Minestrone below a bowl of crusty bread. Back right Pasta Marinara served with Vegetables Creole.

Balinese Spiced Liver

Serves 4

2 small onions, grated
1 garlic clove, crushed
good pinch of ground
   turmeric
2.5 ml (½ tsp) soft brown
   sugar
pinch of ground black
   pepper
20 ml (4 tsp) soy sauce
1 bay leaf
5 ml (1 tsp) finely
   chopped chilli
20 ml (4 tsp) peanut
   butter
juice of ½ lemon
500 g (1 lb) chicken
   livers, sliced
250 ml (8 fl oz, 1 cup)
   coconut milk
garnish: tomato and
   cucumber wedges

Liver should be prepared and eaten the same day. It's one of the richest sources of iron.

Method:

1. Mix all the ingredients, except the chicken livers and coconut milk, to make a soft paste. If the paste is too thick, add a little water. It should have the consistency of yoghurt.
2. In a saucepan, bring the paste to a gentle simmer and cook, stirring frequently, for 5 minutes.
3. Add the chicken livers and cook, stirring gently, until the livers change colour.
4. Add the coconut milk and slowly bring the mixture to the boil, stirring constantly. Reduce the heat and simmer for about 5 minutes until the mixture thickens.
5. Serve hot on a bed of boiled brown rice. Garnish with wedges of tomato and cucumber.

Nutritional data per serve: 1414 kJ (338 cal), CHO 7 g, Protein 31 g, Fat 21 g.

Preparation time: 30 minutes. Cooking equipment: medium saucepan.

Chicken with Strawberry and Peppercorn Sauce

Serves 4

10 ml (2 tsp) oil
4 chicken fillets
1 quantity Strawberry
   and Peppercorn Sauce
   (page 156)
garnish: 4 whole
   strawberries

Some unusual combinations don't quite make the mark but this one is delicious and worthy of a special occasion. You don't have to go to the trouble of fanning the fillets or strawberries in the way we suggest, although this gives a professional touch; simply spoon the sauce over the cooked fillets and garnish them with halved strawberries.

Method:

1. Brush the frying pan with oil and heat over medium heat. Sauté the chicken fillets until cooked and golden brown. (You can microwave them on High for 3 minutes but they will not brown.)

2. Prepare sauce as on page 156.
3. Slice whole strawberries, leaving them joined at the base. Fan out from top of strawberry (optional).
4. Slice fillets through and fan across each plate.
5. Pour sauce over and garnish with fanned strawberries.

To vary: sliced turkey breast with Strawberry and Peppercorn Sauce makes a wonderful and unusual Christmas dinner.

Nutritional data per serve: 922 kJ (237 cal), CHO 7 g, Protein 30 g, Fat 8 g.
Preparation time: 15 minutes (including sauce). Chicken can be cooked while sauce is reducing.
Cooking equipment: large frying pan.

Apricot Chicken

Serves 4

300 g (10 oz, 2 cups)
   canned apricots
4 chicken breasts,
   skinned
1 large onion, chopped
coarsely ground black
   pepper, to taste
2 sage leaves, finely
   chopped or 2.5 ml
   (½ tsp) dried sage
1 thyme sprig, chopped
20 ml (4 tsp) fruit
   chutney
20 ml (4 tsp) cornflour
   (cornstarch)
40 ml (8 tsp) water
garnish: 4 apricot halves
   reserved from main
   quantity
finely snipped chives or
   chopped mint

Method:
1. Reserve four apricot halves for garnish. Purée remaining apricots in a food processor or blender, or press through a sieve.
2. Arrange chicken fillets in a single layer in a casserole. Sprinkle over onion, pepper and herbs.
3. Combine chutney and apricot purée and pour over the chicken. Bake in a preheated oven for 30 minutes.
4. Mix the cornflour (cornstarch) and water to a smooth paste.
5. Remove casserole from oven. Use a slotted spoon to lift out chicken breasts; cover and keep warm.
6. Drain the sauce from the casserole into a saucepan. Add the cornflour (cornstarch) paste to the sauce and heat, stirring constantly, until it thickens. Cook for a further 2 minutes.
7. Arrange a chicken breast on each plate and spoon sauce over each one. Garnish with the reserved apricot halves and sprinkle over the chives or mint.

Nutritional data per serve: 805 kJ (192 cal), CHO 11 g, Protein 26 g, Fat 5 g.

Preparation time: 40 minutes. Cooking equipment: casserole, saucepan, food processor or blender.
Oven temperature: 180 °C (350 °F, gas 4).

Chicken Tikka

Serves 4

200 g (7 oz) low-fat plain
  yoghurt
juice of 1 lemon
5 ml (1 tsp) finely
  chopped or minced
  fresh ginger
5 ml (1 tsp) finely
  chopped or minced
  garlic
good pinch of dried
  coriander
2.5 ml (½ tsp) powdered
  turmeric
40 ml (8 tsp) chopped
  fresh mint
good pinch of ground
  black pepper
good pinch of garam
  masala
4 chicken breasts or
  thighs, skin removed

This is simple to make and superbly fragrant. All you need to add is a carbohydrate-rich accompaniment and steamed vegetables or a crisp salad.

Method:
1. Combine yoghurt, lemon juice and flavourings in a bowl.
2. Add chicken and cover well with marinade. Cover and refrigerate for 2 – 3 hours.
3. Lift chicken from marinade. Place on baking dish. Cover with foil and bake in a preheated oven for 30 minutes.
4. Remove foil, spoon remaining marinade over and bake until chicken is tender and lightly browned (30 – 60 minutes).

Nutritional data per serve: 723 kJ (173 cal), CHO 4 g, Protein 27 g, Fat 6 g.

Preparation time: 2 hours. Cooking equipment: baking dish. Oven temperature: 200 °C (400 °F, gas 6).

Saté Chicken

Serves 4
(3 skewers each)

500 g (1 lb) chicken
  fillets
1 garlic clove, crushed
40 ml (8 tsp) soy sauce
40 ml (8 tsp) lemon juice
1 small onion, grated
5 ml (1 tsp) oil

A Malaysian recipe that makes a great alternative for a barbecue. Prawns, pork, beef and lamb fillet are all delicious cooked with this marinade.

Method:
1. Cut chicken into small cubes.
2. Thread the chicken on to skewers. Arrange the skewers on a flat dish.

3. Combine remaining ingredients and brush over the chicken. Leave the chicken to marinate for at least an hour, turning occasionally.
4. Grill or barbecue the saté chicken, turning frequently and basting from time to time with marinade.
5. Serve hot, accompanied by Peanut Sauce (page 152), Gado Gado (page 87) and brown rice.

To store: use on day of preparation. However, the dish may be made some hours ahead of time and kept, covered, in the refrigerator. You can freeze uncooked saté.

Nutritional data per serve: 708 kJ (169 cal), CHO 1 g, Protein 26 g, Fat 7 g.

Preparation time: 1½ hours (including marinating). Cooking equipment: 12 wooden skewers (soak skewers in water for an hour before using to prevent burning), grill or barbecue.

Golden Chicken Risotto

Serves 4

40 ml (8 tsp) water
1 large onion, chopped
1 garlic clove, crushed
300 g (10 oz, 1½ cups) brown rice
1.5 litres (2¾ pints, 7 cups) Chicken Stock (page 72) or 4 chicken stock cubes dissolved in 1.5 litres (2¾ pints, 7 cups) water
4 chicken breasts, skinned, finely diced
5 ml (1 tsp) powdered turmeric
20 almonds, blanched and halved
45 g (1½ oz, ¼ cup) raisins

There are two ways of preparing this dish — on top of the stove or in the oven; they are equally effective.

Method 1 – Preparing risotto on the hob:
1. In a large saucepan, heat the water to boiling, add the onion and cook until softened.
2. Add the garlic and cook for 2 minutes.
3. Add the rice and one quarter of the chicken stock. Bring to the boil. Reduce heat and simmer for 20 minutes, stirring occasionally and adding more stock, as necessary, to prevent sticking.
4. Add the diced chicken breasts, turmeric, almonds and raisins.
5. Continue simmering for a further 20 – 25 minutes, adding remaining stock as necessary, until the rice is tender. There should be no liquid in the finished risotto.

Method 2 – Preparing risotto in a casserole:
1. Place all ingredients in a casserole.
2. Cover and cook in a preheated oven for 1 hour, or until rice has absorbed the stock and is tender.

Serve hot, accompanied by a green salad.

Nutritional data per serve: 2044 kJ (488 cal), CHO 65 g, Protein 32 g, Fat 11 g.

Preparation time: about 1 hour. Cooking equipment: saucepan, large saucepan or casserole with lid. Oven temperature: 180 °C (350 °F, gas 4).

Chicken with Mustard Seed Sauce

Serves 4

4 chicken fillets, skinned

125 ml (4 fl oz, ½ cup)
   tomato sauce

5 ml (1 tsp) Tabasco

40 ml (8 tsp) whole-grain
   mustard

20 ml (4 tsp)
   Worcestershire sauce

20 ml (4 tsp) malt
   (brown) vinegar

1 clove garlic, crushed

This is so easy to make and, once it's in the oven, you needn't think about it again until you're ready to bring it to the table.

Method:

1. Arrange chicken in casserole.
2. Combine tomato sauce, Tabasco, mustard, Worcestershire sauce, vinegar and garlic.
3. Pour over chicken.
4. Cover and bake in a preheated oven for 45 minutes. Alternatively, cover and microwave on Medium for 35 minutes.
5. Serve with cooked rice and hot vegetables or a salad.

To store: cover and refrigerate for up to two days.

Nutritional data per serve: 749 kJ (179 cal), CHO 3 g, Protein 26 g, Fat 7 g.
Preparation time: 1 hour. Cooking equipment: casserole. Oven temperature: 180 °C (350 °F, gas 4).

Five-spice Chicken

Serves 4

good pinch of Chinese
   five-spice powder

2.5 ml (½ tsp) chilli
   powder (or to taste)

5 ml (1 tsp) soy sauce

1 garlic clove, crushed

175 ml (6 fl oz, ¾ cup)
   low-fat plain yoghurt

4 chicken breasts,
   skinned

Method:

1. Fold five-spice powder, chilli powder, soy sauce and garlic gently into yoghurt.
2. Coat chicken breasts in yoghurt mixture and allow to stand for at least 4 hours.
3. Place in shallow casserole, cover with lid or foil, and bake in a preheated oven for 1 hour or until tender, turning occasionally. Alternatively, microwave, covered, on Medium for 30 minutes or until tender, turning occasionally during the cooking process.

Note: this recipe is better cooked in a conventional oven than in a microwave.

Nutritional data per serve: 736 kJ (176 cal), CHO 4 g, Protein 28 g, Fat 6 g.
Preparation time: 1¼ hours, plus 4 hours marinating time. Cooking equipment: shallow casserole or baking dish. Oven temperature: 150 °C (300 °F, gas 2).

Chicken Enchiladas

Serves 4

300 g (10 oz, 2 cups)
cooked, chopped
chicken breast, skinned

1 small onion, finely
chopped

1 ripe avocado

juice of ½ lemon

8 – 10 drops Tabasco, or
according to taste

good pinch of salt

good pinch of ground
black pepper

4 small wholemeal pitta
breads

450 ml (¾ pint, 2 cups)
fresh tomato purée or
commercial pasta
sauce (meatless)

additional Tabasco to
taste

60 g (2 oz, ½ cup) low-fat
hard cheese, grated

Don't try storing the enchiladas, as they will become soggy. You should serve them immediately they are heated through. Heat them in the oven, not in the microwave.

Method:

1. Combine chicken and onion in mixing bowl.
2. Peel avocado, remove stone. Mash flesh in a separate bowl with lemon juice.
3. Add Tabasco, salt and pepper and add to chicken mixture.
4. Mix well. Taste and adjust seasoning.
5. Split pitta breads in half so there are eight rounds.
6. Wrap each around one-eighth of chicken mixture. Pack into a casserole or baking dish.
7. Combine tomato purée with additional Tabasco and pour over chicken rolls.
8. Sprinkle with cheese.
9. Bake in a preheated oven until rolls are heated through and cheese has melted.

Nutritional data per serve: 2033 kJ (486 cal), CHO 26 g, Protein 39 g, Fat 25 g.

Preparation time: 1 hour. Cooking equipment: saucepan, shallow baking dish or casserole. Oven temperature: 200 °C (400 °F, gas 6).

Chicken Soy

Serves 4

---

*4 spring onions
(shallots), chopped*

2 garlic cloves, crushed

*10 ml (2 tsp) grated fresh
ginger*

*60 ml (2 fl oz, ¼ cup) soy
sauce*

*60 ml (2 fl oz, ¼ cup) dry
sherry*

*4 chicken breasts,
skinned*

*garnish: chopped parsley
or spring onions
(shallots) or snipped
chives*

Try a garnish of sesame seeds added before baking instead of the garnish suggested in the recipe.

Method:

1. Prepare the marinade: in a bowl, combine all the ingredients except the chicken.

2. Arrange the chicken breasts in a baking dish. Pour over the marinade. Cover with clingfilm (plastic wrap) and refrigerate for 2 hours, turning occasionally.

3. Bake, uncovered in a preheated oven for 40 minutes, basting occasionally, or cover and microwave on Medium for 20 – 25 minutes.

4. Remove chicken from baking dish and arrange on a serving platter. Brush with pan juices. Sprinkle parsley, spring onions (shallots) or chives over.

To store: cover and refrigerate for up to three days after cooking. Not recommended for freezing as the chicken dries out.

Nutritional data per serve: 685 kJ (164 cal), CHO 3 g, Protein 26 g, Fat 5 g.

Preparation time: 3 hours, including marinating time. Cooking equipment: baking dish. Oven temperature: 180 °C (350 °F, gas 4).

Drunken Rabbit Casserole

Serves 4

800 g (1 ¾ lb rabbit),
   jointed
5 ml (1 tsp) wine vinegar
   or lemon juice
1 medium onion, sliced
250 ml (8 fl oz, 1 cup)
   water
125 ml (4 fl oz, ½ cup)
   red wine
2 chicken stock cubes,
   crumbled
20 ml (4 tsp) tomato
   paste
2 medium tomatoes,
   chopped
2.5 ml (½ tsp) dried
   oregano
6 spring onions
   (shallots), chopped
16 small button
   mushrooms
20 ml (4 tsp) cornflour
   (cornstarch)
20 ml (4 tsp) water

If rabbit is unavailable, you can use lean chicken instead. You'll need about 500 g (1 lb) chicken breast.

Method:

1. Soak rabbit in cold water with a teaspoon of vinegar or lemon juice for 30 minutes. Discard water.
2. In a casserole, combine the rabbit, onion, 250 ml (8 fl oz, 1 cup) water, wine, stock cubes, tomato paste, chopped tomatoes and oregano. Cover and bake in a preheated oven for 1 1/4 hours, or microwave on Medium for 30 – 40 minutes.
3. Remove casserole from oven. Add the spring onions (shallots) and mushrooms and stir in. Cover, return to oven and bake for a further 15 minutes or microwave on High for 5 minutes.
4. Remove casserole from oven. Using a slotted spoon, lift the rabbit and vegetables on to a serving platter; cover and keep warm.
5. Pour the juices into a saucepan.
6. In a cup, stir the cornflour (cornstarch) and 20 ml (4 tsp) water to make a smooth paste and add to the cooking juices. Bring to the boil, stirring constantly, until thickened. Reduce heat and simmer for 2 minutes.
7. Pour the sauce over the rabbit and vegetables and serve at once.

To store: cover and refrigerate for up to three days.

Nutritional data per serve: 997 kJ (238 cal), CHO 12 g, Protein 30 g, Fat 8 g.
Preparation time: 2 ¼ hours. Cooking equipment: casserole with lid, medium saucepan.
Oven temperature: 180 °C (350 °F, gas 4).

Sweet and Sour Rabbit with Prunes

Serves 4

800 g (1¾ lb) rabbit,
   jointed
250 ml (8 fl oz, 1 cup)
   dry white wine
2 medium onions, peeled
   and sliced
350 ml (12 fl oz, 1½ cups)
   Chicken Stock (page
   72) or 350 ml
   (12 fl oz, 1½ cups)
   water and 2 chicken
   stock cubes
1 bay leaf
20 ml (4 tsp) redcurrant
   jelly
6 – 8 peppercorns,
   according to taste
8 whole prunes, stoned
45 g (1½ oz, ¼ cup)
   seedless raisins
20 ml (4 tsp) malt
   vinegar
40 ml (8 tsp) cornflour
   (cornstarch)
freshly ground black
   pepper
garnish: chopped parsley

Rabbit is low in fat and easy to prepare.

Method:

1. Marinate rabbit overnight in the wine and onions.
2. Discard the onions, place the rabbit and wine marinade in a flameproof casserole and add the chicken stock, bay leaf, redcurrant jelly and peppercorns; bring to the boil. Turn down the heat.
3. Add the prunes and raisins, submerge them in the cooking liquid, cover the casserole tightly and bake in a preheated oven for about 1 1/2 hours until the rabbit is tender and the prunes are plump.
4. Remove from oven, lift out the rabbit and remove the bones. Set meat aside and strain the cooking juices into a clean pan, retaining the prunes and raisins.
5. Blend cornflour (cornstarch) with vinegar to form a smooth paste, add to juices and boil for 1 – 2 minutes, stirring all the time until the sauce thickens. Arrange the rabbit, prunes and raisins in the casserole and pour the thickened juices over. Garnish with parsley.

Nutritional data per serve: 1152 kJ (275 cal), CHO 17 g, Protein 32 g, Fat 9 g.

Preparation time: 2 hours plus overnight soaking. Cooking equipment: large flameproof casserole with lid, medium saucepan. Oven temperature: 160 °C (325 °F, gas 3).

Meatless Dishes

Jumping Bean Bake

*Serves 4 as a main
course, 8 as a
side dish*

---

*410 g (14 oz, 2 cups)
dried beans (any
variety) or 800 g
(1¾ lb, 4 cups) canned
and drained beans
such as lima,
bortolotti, kidney, soy
or haricot*

*250 ml (8 fl oz, 1 cup)
tomato purée*

*good pinch of cayenne
pepper*

2 garlic cloves, crushed

*5 ml (1 tsp) dried
oregano*

1 bay leaf

*500 g (1 lb) ripe
tomatoes, sliced*

2 medium onions, sliced

Topping:

*30 g (1 oz, ½ cup) fresh
wholemeal
breadcrumbs*

*45 g (1½ oz) low-fat hard
cheese, grated*

For a thicker version of this dish, mash half the beans and leave the rest whole at Step 1 of the method described below.

Method:

1. Place dried beans in a saucepan, cover with water and soak overnight (note: do not soak the beans in an aluminium saucepan). Next day, drain the beans and rinse them thoroughly in cold water. Return them to the saucepan and cover with fresh water. Bring to the boil, reduce heat and simmer, loosely covered, for 1 hour or until tender, or microwave on High for 5 minutes, then Medium-low for 30 minutes or until tender. Drain beans, discarding water. If you are using canned beans, drain them and rinse them well.

2. In a bowl, combine the tomato purée, cayenne pepper, garlic and herbs.

3. Grease the casserole lightly and place a layer of beans on the base, cover with a layer of tomatoes and then a layer of onions. Repeat the layers until all the ingredients are used.

4. Pour tomato mixture over top with breadcrumbs and cheese.

5. Cover and bake in a preheated oven for 1 hour, then remove cover and bake for another hour or until beans start to break apart. Alternatively, cover and microwave on Medium for 45 minutes, then remove the cover and microwave for another 30 minutes or until the beans start to break apart.

6. Serve immediately.

To store: cover and refrigerate for up to two days.

Nutritional data per serve (main meal): 1601 kJ (382 cal), CHO 55 g, Protein 29 g, Fat 4 g.
Preparation time: 2¼ hours after you have soaked the beans overnight.
Cooking equipment: medium saucepan, deep casserole. Oven temperature: 180 °C (350 °F, gas 4).

Vegetable Loaf

Serves 6

40 ml (8 tsp) water

2 medium onions,
   chopped

2 celery sticks, chopped

½ green pepper
   (capsicum), chopped

10 ml (2 tsp) Curry
   Powder (page 162)

100 g (3 ½ oz, ½ cup)
   cooked, mashed potato

125 g (4 oz, ½ cup)
   cooked, mashed
   pumpkin

250 g (8 oz, 1 cup) ricotta
   cheese

125 g (4 oz, 1 cup)
   coarsely ground
   cashew nuts

45 g (1 ½ oz, ½ cup)
   rolled oats

40 ml (8 tsp) chopped
   parsley

5 ml (1 tsp) chopped
   fresh thyme or 2.5 ml
   (½ tsp) dried

garnish: 40 ml (8 tsp)
   sesame seeds

To serve:

1 quantity Cheese Sauce
   (page 152) or Fresh
   Vegetable Sauce
   (page 153)

This loaf is very high in fibre and is delicious eaten hot or cold with one of the sauces we recommend.

Method:

1. In a frying pan, or in a bowl in the microwave oven, heat the water and sauté onions, celery, pepper (capsicum) and Curry Powder for 3 minutes.

2. In a bowl, combine the sautéed vegetables with the rest of the ingredients.

3. Line a loaf tin with foil and oil it lightly.

4. Sprinkle sesame seeds over base of tin and then shake tin so that seeds adhere to sides as well.

5. Spoon vegetable mixture into the tin and press down firmly and neatly.

6. Bake in a preheated oven for 40 minutes.

7. Remove from oven and leave to stand for 5 minutes before turning out. Turn on to serving dish and remove foil carefully.

8. Finally, place under a hot grill for 3 – 5 minutes or until the top is crisp and well browned.

To serve: cut loaf into thick slices but do not separate them; spoon hot sauce over.

To store: cover and refrigerate for up to four days.

Nutritional data per serve: 1781 kJ (425 cal), CHO 25 g, Protein 29 g, Fat 24 g.

Preparation time: 1 hour plus preparation time for sauce.
Cooking equipment: frying pan, loaf tin 20 x 10 cm (8 x 4 inches).
Oven temperature: 180 °C (350 °F, gas 4, hot grill).

Foreground: simple lettuce salad, centre sweetcorn, mangetout (snow peas) and red pepper (capsicum) with Curried Tuna and Rice Casserole. Top left Fruit Crumble and Custard Sauce. Fresh pears at top right.

Vegetarian Lasagne

Serves 4 – 6

Sauce:

oil

*2 medium onions, peeled
and chopped*

*3 large tomatoes,
chopped*

150 g (5 oz) tomato paste

*450 ml (¾ pint, 2 cups)
water*

*2.5 – 5 ml (1 – 2 tsp)
crushed or finely
chopped garlic*

*5 ml (1 tsp) dried mixed
herbs*

*good pinch each of black
pepper and salt*

*750 g (1 ½ lb) canned
kidney beans*

Layers:

*250 g (8 oz) frozen
spinach*

*9 sheets instant spinach
or wholemeal lasagne
noodles*

*125 g (4 oz, ½ cup)
cottage cheese*

*60 g (2 oz, ½ cup) grated
low-fat hard cheese*

*40 ml (8 tsp) grated
Parmesan cheese*

This dish is even better if prepared the day before it is to be served, so that the flavour can fully develop. It freezes well, so prepare a few and store them in the freezer as a standby.

Method:

1. Wipe a frying pan with oil, heat it and sauté onions in frying pan until lightly browned, stirring to prevent burning.
2. Add tomatoes and cook for about 5 minutes until soft.
3. Add tomato paste and water and mix thoroughly.
4. Add seasonings.
5. Rinse and drain beans and add. Combine well.
6. Simmer gently, covered, until you are ready to assemble the lasagne. If sauce becomes too thick, add a little water.
7. Place spinach in saucepan. Cook very gently, uncovered, until it is fairly dry.

To assemble:

8. Spoon a thin layer of tomato and bean sauce over base of dish.
9. Arrange a layer of noodles on top.
10. Spoon on more sauce, sprinkle with half the cottage cheese and hard cheese and 20 ml (4 tsp) of Parmesan.
11. Top with another layer of noodles and cover this with spinach, the remaining cottage cheese, hard cheese and Parmesan.
12. Place the last layer of noodles over this, cover with the remaining sauce and, lastly, sprinkle with the remaining grated hard cheese.
13. Cover with foil and bake in a preheated oven for 30 minutes. Remove the foil, and bake for a further 30 minutes or until noodles are tender.

Nutritional data per serve (to serve 5): 1369 kJ (327 cal), CHO 42 g, Protein 25 g, Fat 6 g.

Preparation time: 2 hours. Cooking equipment: frying pan, small saucepan, square baking dish. Oven temperature: 180 °C (350 °F, gas 4).

Foreground: Paella accompanied by Spinach Valentino. Olives at centre and Mussels à la Grecque at the top.

Tibetan Pie

Serves 6

1 quantity Wholemeal
    Pastry (page 186)
Filling:
500 g (1 lb) frozen
    spinach
6 medium potatoes,
    washed but not peeled,
    cut into large pieces
1 large onion, chopped
15 g (½ oz, ⅓ cup)
    chopped fresh mixed
    herbs (mint, thyme,
    parsley, oregano,
    marjoram)
2.5 ml (½ tsp) coarsely
    ground black pepper
5 ml (1 tsp) salt
    (optional)
good pinch of grated
    nutmeg
5 ml (1 tsp) curry powder
10 ml (2 tsp) margarine

Keep pastry cool in the refrigerator while preparing the filling; this prevents the pastry from becoming soggy when you add hot filling.

Method:
1. Cook spinach in saucepan until excess water has evaporated. The spinach should be fairly dry.
2. Boil potatoes until tender. Drain and mash potatoes roughly so that some pieces remain.
3. Add spinach, onion, herbs, spices and margarine.
4. Cut pastry into two pieces (two-thirds and one-third).
5. Roll out larger piece to cover base and sides of pie dish.
6. Spoon filling on to pastry, brush pastry edge with a little water.
7. Roll out smaller piece of pastry. Place on top of filling. Pierce the top of the pastry with a fork.
8. Trim the pastry to size and pinch the edges of pastry together.
9. Bake in a preheated oven for about 45 minutes or until lightly browned.

Nutritional data per serve: 1776 kJ (424 cal), CHO 50 g, Protein 12 g, Fat 19 g.

Preparation time: 1 ½ hours. Cooking equipment: 2 saucepans, pie dish. Oven temperature: 200 °C (400 °F, gas 6).

Spanish Omelette

Serves 5

10 ml (2 tsp) margarine
3 medium potatoes,
    diced but not peeled
1 large onion, chopped
6 mushrooms, chopped
1 green pepper
    (capsicum), chopped

Delicious cold or hot, this is a great way of using up leftover cooked and uncooked vegetables. It also makes a nutritious packed lunch.

Method:
1. Melt margarine in frying pan over medium-high heat.
2. Add potato and onion. Cover and cook over low heat for about 15 minutes until potatoes are tender.
3. Add mushrooms, pepper (capsicum), cooked vegetables and celery and cook for a further 5 minutes.

90 g (3 oz, ½ cup) cooked
   vegetables (sweetcorn,
   peas, carrots)
½ celery stick, chopped
5 eggs
good pinch each of black
   pepper and grated
   nutmeg
5 ml (1 tsp) dried mixed
   herbs
pinch of salt (optional)
10 ml (2 tsp) chopped
   parsley
few drops of Tabasco or
   pinch of cayenne pepper
60 ml (2 fl oz, ¼ cup)
   water

4. Beat eggs with seasoning, herbs and water.
5. Pour over vegetables in frying pan, cover and cook over low heat until almost set. Do not allow base to burn.
6. Preheat grill to medium and slide omelette under the grill to complete cooking.
7. Loosen omelette and turn on to warm plate.
8. Cut into wedges to serve.

Nutritional data per serve: 688 kJ (164 cal), CHO 16 g, Protein 10 g, Fat 7 g.

Preparation time: 30 minutes. Cooking equipment: large heavy-based frying pan.

Vegetable Curry

Serves 4

500 g (1 lb) mixed
   vegetables
10 ml (2 tsp) oil
1 onion, sliced
5 ml (1 tsp) ground
   turmeric
2.5 ml (½ tsp) ground
   cumin
2 cm (¾ inch) piece fresh
   ginger, chopped
2 garlic cloves, chopped
1 or 2 fresh hot chillies
   (optional) or chilli
   powder to taste
250 ml (8 fl oz, 1 cup)
   water
250 ml (8 fl oz, 1 cup)
   coconut milk
20 ml (4 tsp) lemon juice

Use a variety of vegetables to make this an economical dish based on whatever vegetables are in season. Beans, cabbage, broccoli, cauliflower, pumpkin, sweet potatoes, spinach, potatoes, peas, carrots, aubergine (eggplant) and courgettes (zucchini, baby marrow) are ideal.

Method:
1. Trim vegetables and cut into pieces.
2. Heat oil until very hot in wok or large frying pan.
3. Add onion and spices and toss until onion is golden brown.
4. Add the rest of the vegetables and stir-fry for 2 – 3 minutes.
5. Add 250 ml (8 fl oz, 1 cup) of water and cook for 6 – 8 minutes, uncovered, or until vegetables are tender.
6. Add coconut milk and bring to the boil.
7. Remove from heat. Add lemon juice.
8. Serve with brown rice.

Nutritional data per serve: 657 kJ (157 cal), CHO 8 g, Protein 4 g, Fat 12 g.

Preparation time: 45 minutes. Cooking equipment: wok or large frying pan.

Semolina Gnocchi with Tomato and Basil Sauce

Serves 4

350 ml (12 fl oz,
   1 ½ cups) skimmed or
   low-fat milk

2.5 ml (½ tsp) grated
   nutmeg

150 g (5 oz, 1 cup)
   semolina

2 eggs, beaten

small amount of plain
   flour

250 ml (8 fl oz, 1 cup)
   Tomato and Basil
   Sauce (page 155) or
   250 ml (8 fl oz, 1 cup)
   commercial tomato-
   based pasta sauce

Gnocchi are best served fresh but they can be refrigerated for up to three days and then reheated in boiling water. Or prepare the gnocchi to Step 5 then freeze; complete the preparations from Step 6 when you need to serve them.

Method:

1. Place milk and nutmeg in medium saucepan and bring to the boil. Remove from heat and quickly stir in semolina.
2. Return to heat and stir for one minute.
3. Add eggs and work into a smooth dough.
4. Break off small, even-sized pieces about the size of a walnut, roll into balls and toss in a little flour.
5. Half fill a large saucepan with water and bring to the boil.
6. Drop gnocchi into boiling water and cook for about 5 minutes (gnocchi will rise to the top of the water as they cook).
7. Drain, toss in sauce and serve immediately.

Nutritional data per serve: 1076 kJ (257 cal), CHO 38 g, Protein 12 g, Fat 6 g.

Preparation time: 30 minutes plus preparation time for sauce.
Cooking equipment: medium saucepan, a large saucepan.

Potato Gnocchi

Serves 4

500 g (1 lb) potatoes,
   peeled, cooked and
   mashed

60 g (2 oz, ½ cup) plain
   flour

60 g (2 oz, ½ cup)
   wholemeal flour

1 quantity Fresh
   Vegetable Sauce
   (page 153)

45 g (1½ oz) low-fat hard
   cheese, grated

You can prepare gnocchi to Step 3 and then freeze them. When you are ready to use the gnocchi, drop them into boiling water and follow the recipe from Step 4.

Method:

1. Half-fill saucepan with water and bring to the boil. A little salt may be added to the cooking water if desired.
2. Mix potato with both flours, then turn on to a floured board and knead gently until smooth.
3. Divide mixture into four and roll each into a sausage about 2 cm (^{3}⁄4 inch) in diameter. Cut lengths into 2 cm (^{3}⁄4 inch) pieces and drop into boiling water.

4. Boil gently for 8 – 10 minutes until gnocchi are light and cooked (gnocchi will rise to surface of the water as they cook).
5. Use a slotted spoon to remove on to a serving dish.
6. Toss in sauce, sprinkle with cheese and serve immediately.

To vary: sprinkle with chopped lean ham or use tomato and basil sauce instead of Fresh Vegetable Sauce.

Nutritional data per serve: 1222 kJ (292 cal), CHO 50 g, Protein 14 g, Fat 4 g.

Preparation time: 15 minutes plus preparation time for sauce. Cooking equipment: large saucepan.

Pitta Pizza

Serves 4

4 small wholemeal pitta breads
250 ml (8 fl oz, 1 cup) Tomato and Basil Sauce (page 155) or 250 ml (8 fl oz, 1 cup) commercial pasta sauce
3 large tomatoes, sliced
1 medium green pepper (capsicum), seeded and sliced
75 g (2 ½ oz, 1 cup) sliced mushrooms
1 medium onion, peeled and sliced
90 g (3 oz) low-fat hard cheese, grated
oil
16 black olives, chopped (optional)
1 courgette (zucchini, baby marrow), sliced (optional)

The beauty of this recipe is that by using pitta bread as the pizza base, you can put the whole dish together very quickly. These pizzas freeze well, making them an ideal snack or light meal.

Method:
1. Spread pitta breads with sauce. Arrange the vegetables evenly over the top and sprinkle with grated cheese.
2. Place on a lightly oiled baking sheet. Bake in a preheated oven until cheese melts and begins to brown.
3. Serve pitta pizzas straight from the oven, accompanied by a Tossed Salad (page 150).

To store: prepare pizzas in advance up to Step 2, wrap in clingfilm (plastic wrap) or slide into big freezer bags and freeze until needed; then place the frozen pizzas on a baking sheet and bake for 25 minutes.

Nutritional data per serve: 1404 kJ (335 cal), CHO 42 g, Protein 17 g, Fat 11 g.

Preparation time: 30 minutes plus preparation time for sauce. Cooking equipment: large saucepan, baking sheet. Oven temperature: 180 °C (350 °F, gas 4).

Cheese and Spinach Rolls

Serves 4

1 bunch fresh spinach or
   250 g (8 oz) frozen
   spinach
40 ml (8 tsp) water
4 spring onions
   (shallots), chopped
250 g (8 oz, 1 cup) ricotta
   cheese
150 g (5 oz, 1 cup) cooked
   brown rice
40 ml (8 tsp) lemon juice
pinch of grated nutmeg
12 sheets filo pastry
40 ml (8 tsp) skimmed
   milk

Serve these fragrant rolls with Cheese Sauce (page 152) spooned over them. Try adding 40 ml (8 tsp) pine nuts or chopped walnuts to the filling mixture.

Method:

1. Wash fresh spinach very thoroughly under cold, running water. Do not dry it. Chop roughly. Place wet, chopped spinach in a large saucepan. Cover and cook over high heat for about 10 minutes or until tender. Remove spinach from saucepan and drain well. Set aside to cool. If you are using frozen spinach, cook it, uncovered, in a saucepan over low heat until excess water has evaporated; set aside to cool.
2. Bring water to the boil in a saucepan, add the spring onions (shallots) and cook until softened.
3. Combine onions with spinach, cheese, rice, lemon juice and nutmeg and blend well.
4. Fold a sheet of filo pastry in half widthwise. Brush lightly with milk.
5. Repeat with another two sheets of filo. Place them on top of the first and brush milk between each sheet. You now have six layers of pastry.
6. Place a quarter of the filling along the edge of the pastry and roll up to enclose the filling. Lift and tuck in the ends of the pastry before the last roll. This makes a neat parcel.
7. Place the completed roll, seal-side down, on a lightly greased baking sheet.
8. Repeat Steps 4 to 7 to make four cheese and spinach rolls.
9. Brush each roll with milk. Bake in a preheated oven for 15 minutes or until pastry is crisp and golden.

To store: cover and refrigerate for up to three days.

Freezing: do not allow the rolls to brown too much during cooking as they will colour further when reheated. Freeze cooked rolls in suitable containers. Thaw completely before reheating.

Nutritional data per serve: 1139 kJ (272 cal), CHO 37 g, Protein 14 g, Fat 7 g.

Preparation time: 45 minutes. Cooking equipment: medium saucepan, baking sheet.
Oven temperature: 200 °C (400 °F, gas 6).

Mexicale Pie with Cornmeal Dumplings

Serves 4

10 ml (2 tsp) oil

1 onion, finely chopped

2 garlic cloves, crushed

1 green pepper
    (capsicum), diced

40 ml (8 tsp) tomato paste

410 g (14 oz) can whole
    tomatoes

410 g (14 oz) canned
    sweetcorn kernels,
    drained

750 g (1 ½ lb) canned
    kidney beans, drained

2.5 ml (½ tsp) allspice

5 ml (1 tsp) chilli
    powder, or to taste

1 bay leaf

10 ml (2 tsp)
    Worcestershire sauce

125 ml (4 fl oz, ½ cup)
    water

Cornmeal dumpling
    mixture:

125 g (4 oz, 1 cup) each
    wholemeal self-raising
    flour and polenta
    (yellow cornmeal)

175 ml (6 fl oz, ¾ cup)
    low-fat milk

2 eggs, lightly beaten

125 g (4 oz, 1 cup) grated
    low-fat hard cheese

40 ml (8 tsp) snipped
    chives

This dish is partlicularly high in Carbohydrates. Experiment with the flavourings according to your taste for spicy food. We have suggested canned vegetables and beans to make the dish quick to prepare.

Method:

1. Heat oil in the saucepan over medium heat and then sauté onion, garlic and pepper (capsicum) for about 3 minutes until just tender.
2. Add tomato paste, vegetables, spices, bay leaf, Worcestershire sauce and water.
3. Boil, uncovered, for 15 minutes, then remove bay leaf.
4. Transfer bean mixture to baking dish or casserole.
5. Make the dumplings by combining all the ingredients. Drop spoonfuls of dumpling mixture on top of the bean mixture.
6. Bake, uncovered in a preheated oven for 10 minutes, then reduce heat and bake for a further 30 minutes. Serve hot.

Nutritional data per serve: 3160 kJ (755 cal), CHO 99 g, Protein 48 g, Fat 17 g.

Preparation time: 1¼ hours. Cooking equipment: saucepan, shallow baking dish or casserole. Oven temperature: 200 °C (400 °F, gas 6), then 180 °C (350 °F, gas 4).

Spinach Fettuccine

Serves 4

2 bunches fresh spinach
  or 500 g (1 lb) frozen
  spinach
250 g (8 oz) spinach
  fettuccine
40 ml (8 tsp) pine nuts
20 ml (4 tsp) water
1 small onion, finely
  chopped
½ clove garlic, crushed
5 ml (1 tsp) chopped
  fresh basil, or 2.5 ml
  (½ tsp) dried basil
coarsely ground black
  pepper to taste
250 g (8 oz) ricotta cheese

This dish should always be eaten freshly prepared.

Method:

1. Trim away the roots and woody ends of stems of fresh spinach. Rinse spinach thoroughly in cold, running water but do not dry. Heat a large saucepan. Put the spinach into the saucepan, cover and cook over medium-high heat for 5 – 8 minutes, or until tender. Remove from heat and drain in a colander. Set aside. If you are using frozen spinach, place it in a saucepan and thaw over low-medium heat. Remove from heat, drain well and squeeze to remove excess liquid. Set aside.

2. Fill a large saucepan to two-thirds with water and bring to a rapid boil. Add the fettuccine and boil for 10 – 12 minutes or until it is *al dente* (tender, but firm to bite). Drain.

3. Meanwhile, in a dry frying pan, brown the pine nuts over medium heat, stirring constantly to ensure even colouring and prevent burning. Remove from frying pan and set aside.

4. Return frying pan to the heat. Add 20 ml (4 tsp) water, onion, garlic, basil and pepper. Cook over low heat until the onion is translucent.

5. In a large saucepan, combine the cooked spinach, pine nuts, ricotta cheese and the onion mixture. Add the fettuccine, use two forks to gently lift and turn mixture to combine well.

6. Serve hot.

Nutritional data per serve: 1573 kJ (375 cal), CHO 47 g, Protein 20 g, Fat 11 g.

Preparation time: 30 minutes. Cooking equipment: 2 large saucepans, frying pan.

Claytons Quiche

Serves 4

4 eggs

250 ml (8 fl oz, 1 cup) skimmed milk

250 ml (8 fl oz, 1 cup) full-cream plain yoghurt

40 ml (8 tsp) wholemeal flour

250 g (8 oz, 1 cup) ricotta cheese

60 g (2 oz, ½ cup) chopped spring onions (shallots)

125 g (4 oz) mushrooms, sliced

1 medium tomato, diced
oil

330 g (11 oz) canned asparagus, drained

This quiche makes its own crust. It is quick and easy to make and is delicious hot or cold, served with crusty bread and green salad. It will keep in the refrigerator for up to three days.

Method:

1. Beat together eggs, milk, yoghurt and flour.
2. Add cheese, spring onions (shallots), mushrooms and tomato.
3. Pour into a lightly oiled flan dish.
4. Arrange asparagus on top.
5. Bake in a preheated oven for 30 – 35 minutes or until quiche is set and lightly browned.

Nutritional data per serve: 1146 kJ (274 cal), CHO 15 g, Protein 23 g, Fat 14 g.

Preparation time: 1 hour. Cooking equipment: flan dish. Oven temperature: 180 °C (350 °F, gas 4).

Bubble and Squeak

Serves 4

10 ml (2 tsp) oil

1 medium onion, finely sliced

625 g (1¼ lb, 4 cups) cooked, mixed vegetables (e.g. potato, cabbage, pumpkin, carrot, cauliflower, broccoli, beans, peas, spinach)

black pepper to taste

Method:

1. In a frying pan, heat the oil. Add the onion and sauté gently until lightly browned.
2. Add mixed vegetables and pepper. Use a metal spatula to lift and turn mixture until well combined. Press down vegetables to make a flat cake in the frying pan.
3. Cook over medium heat for 5 minutes, or until the base of the 'cake' is well browned.
4. Cut into wedges in the frying pan. Serve brown-side up.

Nutritional data per serve: 445 kJ (106 cal), CHO 13 g, Protein 7 g, Fat 3 g.

Preparation time: starting with pre-cooked vegetables, 10 minutes. Cooking equipment: large frying pan.

Vegetable Side Dishes

Vegetables tended in the past to be a neglected part of the meal, yet with a little imagination they can be a feature.

Try mixing vegetables in different combinations and experiment by adding fresh or dried herbs and seasonings. Nutmeg, curry powder, onion, chives, tomato, garlic, wine or a sprinkling of toasted sesame seeds or almonds provide a delicious flavour boost. The following ideas may help get you started on a new appreciation of the versatility of vegetables. All the serving suggestions are for four people.

Braised Onion

Place 250 ml (8 fl oz, 1 cup) water and a chicken stock cube in a saucepan and bring to the boil. Add four small peeled and sliced onions and simmer them for about 8 minutes until they are tender. Lift out the onions and set them aside, add 40 ml (8 tsp) dry white wine to the stock and boil the liquid until it is reduced to about 60 ml (2 fl oz). Add the onions, heat through and serve them garnished with snipped chives or chopped parsley.

Braised Lettuce

Wash an iceberg lettuce and remove any stalks or damaged outside leaves. Cut the lettuce into wedges. Bring 450 ml (3/4 pint, 2 cups) chicken stock to the boil, drop in the lettuce wedges and simmer them for 15 – 20 seconds. Lift them out, and if liked, serve them garnished with finely sliced spring onion (shallot) tops.

Lemon Broccoli

Wash one large head of broccoli, removing the woody stem. Cut the broccoli into even florets and steam or boil them for 4 – 6 minutes until they are tender but still crisp. Drain the broccoli. Alternatively, microwave them on High for 4 minutes. Finally, toss them in a mixture of lemon juice, the rind of one lemon and 10 ml (2 tsp) toasted sesame seeds.

Spinach and Spring Onions

Wash a bunch of fresh spinach under running water; remove all trace of dirt. Remove any woody stalks and chop the spinach finely. Place it in a saucepan with a bunch of chopped spring onions (shallots), 40 ml (8 tsp) finely chopped parsley, a pinch of grated nutmeg and 40 ml (8 tsp) water. Cover and cook for 5 – 6 minutes. Alternatively, cover and microwave it on High for 4 – 5 minutes. Serve immediately.

Diced Potatoes with Parsley

Scrub four medium potatoes and cut them into 2 cm (3/4 inch) cubes. Drop them into boiling water and simmer gently for 8 – 10 minutes until tender. Drain. Alternatively, microwave them on High for 7 – 8 minutes. Finally, sprinkle them with parsley and toss gently.

Mangetout (Snow Peas) and Asparagus

Cut 20 asparagus spears to about the length of the mangetout (snow peas), discarding the woody ends. Plunge the asparagus (from which you have removed the stalks) into boiling water for 2 minutes until the asparagus spears are tender. Add 20 mangetout (snow peas), return to the boil and then drain; make sure that the vegetables don't overcook. Place them on a serving dish and sprinkle them with toasted sesame seeds or almond slivers.

This recipe can be varied by replacing the asparagus with whole green beans or celery strips. These vegetables are microwaved on High for 2 – 3 minutes.

Succotash (peas, pepper (capsicum) and sweetcorn)

Boil or steam 125 – 170 g (4 – 6 oz, 1 – 11/2 cups) each of frozen peas and sweetcorn kernels for 4 – 5 minutes. Drain. Alternatively, cover and microwave them on High for 4 minutes. Add a diced red pepper (capsicum), mix thoroughly, season with freshly ground black pepper and serve.

Pumpkin and Mushrooms

Peel and seed four medium pieces of pumpkin and slice each into pieces about 12 mm (1/2 inch) thick. Place them in a saucepan with six sliced mushrooms, 250 ml (8 fl oz, 1 cup) of unsweetened tomato juice, a crushed garlic clove and ground black pepper. Simmer gently for about 15 minutes until the vegetables are tender or, alternatively, place all the ingredients in a microwave dish, cover and microwave on High for 8 minutes.

Courgette (Zucchini, Baby Marrow) and Carrot Rings

Trim and thickly slice four medium courgettes (zucchini, baby marrows) and cut half a medium carrot into thin rings. Heat 10 ml (2 tsp) oil in a large saucepan, add the carrots and cook, tossing constantly, for 2 minutes. Add the courgettes (zucchini, baby marrows) and cook, tossing constantly, for a further 2 minutes. Add 125 ml (4 fl oz, 1/2 cup) water, cover and cook for about 5 minutes until tender. Drain and season with ground black pepper and chopped parsley.

Leek and Apple

Wash and slice a large leek. Peel and slice a large cooking apple. Heat 20 ml (4 tsp) water in a saucepan, add the leek and apple and toss them to mix. Cover and cook over low heat for about 8 minutes until tender. Alternatively, microwave the leek, apple and water on High for 5 minutes.

Vegetables Creole

Peel and quarter a medium onion and cut half a medium green pepper (capsicum) into strips. Place them and 40 ml (8 tsp) water in a saucepan and cook for 2 minutes. Add four quartered tomatoes, four courgettes (zucchini, baby marrows) cut into wedges, 12 pitted black olives and 2.5 ml (1/2 tsp) chopped fresh basil, cover and simmer gently for 10 minutes.

Scalloped Potatoes

Serves 4

6 medium potatoes,
  scrubbed
250 ml (8 fl oz, 1 cup)
  skimmed milk
good pinch of coarsely
  ground black pepper
5 ml (1 tsp) chopped
  parsley
good pinch of dried
  mixed herbs

This is an ideal dish, high in complex carbohydrate. It is wonderfully satisfying just as it is but lends itself equally to tempting variations. We have given two options but you can experiment with your own. Although scalloped potatoes are usually eaten hot, they can also be served cold.

Method:

1. Slice potatoes finely. Arrange in overlapping rows or circles in a shallow baking dish.
2. Pour over skimmed milk and sprinkle with pepper, parsley and herbs.
3. Bake in a preheated oven for 30 minutes or until potatoes are tender and slightly browned on top, or microwave, covered, on High for 20 minutes.

As an accompaniment: serve hot with meat, fish or chicken.

To vary: omit mixed herbs and sprinkle with paprika to taste or, after the potatoes have been in the oven for 25 minutes, remove them and sprinkle them with grated, low-fat hard cheese, then return to the oven for 5 minutes or until the topping is golden and bubbling.

To store: cover and refrigerate for up to two days.

Nutritional data per serve: 566 kJ (135 cal), CHO 26 g, Protein 7 g, Fat trace.
Preparation time: 35 minutes. Cooking equipment: shallow, medium baking dish.
Oven temperature: 180 °C (350 °F, gas 4).

Jacket Potatoes

Serves 4 as an accompaniment; 2 as a light meal

4 medium-sized potatoes

Method:

1. Wash potatoes well; do not peel. Prick several times with a fork or skewer. For a crispy skin: do not cover. For a softer skin: wrap potatoes in foil.
2. Bake the potatoes in a preheated oven for 45 – 60 minutes or until tender when tested with a skewer.

Alternatively, wash the potatoes, prick with a fork and cook, uncovered, in the microwave on High for 12 minutes, turning them over half-way through cooking.

Serve plain or try some of the following delicious fillings, or a combination of your own.

Preparation time: 70 minutes. Cooking equipment: baking sheet.
Oven temperature: 180 °C (350 ˚C, gas 4).

Cheese and pastrami

Slice tops off potatoes and scoop out flesh, leaving four firm shells. Cut two small, thin slices of pastrami into fine strips and mix with 60 g (2 oz, 1/2 cup) grated low-fat hard cheese, the flesh from potatoes and 40 ml (8 tsp) low-fat milk. Add a little ground pepper, spoon back into potato shells and reheat in oven for about 5 – 10 minutes.

Cottage cheese (or yoghurt) and chives

Split open tops of potatoes and place 10 ml (2 tsp) cottage cheese or low-fat plain yoghurt in each. Sprinkle with snipped chives and serve immediately.

Tomato and onion

Sauté one finely-chopped onion in a little water, add one medium tomato, chopped, 2.5 ml (1/2 tsp) fresh basil or oregano and a pinch of ground black pepper. Mix with flesh from potatoes, spoon into potato shells and reheat in oven for about 5 – 10 minutes.

Spicy yoghurt

Combine the flesh of potatoes with 40 ml (8 tsp) low-fat natural yoghurt and a pinch each of ground ginger, cinnamon and cloves. Spoon back into potato shells and reheat in oven for about 5 – 10 minutes.

Duchess Potatoes

Serves 4

4 medium floury
  potatoes
1 egg
5 ml (1 tsp) margarine
white pepper to taste
pinch of salt (optional)
garnish: grated nutmeg

Method:
1. Wash, peel and rinse potatoes.
2. Cut into even-sized pieces.
3. Place in small quantity of boiling water and cook until soft (about 20 minutes) or microwave on High, covered, until soft.
4. Drain and mash potatoes.
5. Beat egg and set aside 5 ml (1 tsp) for glazing.
6. Beat potatoes, margarine and egg together until fluffy.
7. Season with pepper (and salt, if desired).
8. Pipe on to a baking sheet to form cone shapes.
9. Glaze with remaining egg.
10. Sprinkle with grated nutmeg.
11. Brown in a preheated oven for 10 minutes.

Nutritional data per serve: 425 kJ (102 cal), CHO 15 g, Protein 5 g, Fat 2 g.

Preparation time: 30 – 40 minutes. Cooking equipment: saucepan, baking sheet, piping bag and nozzles. Oven temperature: 200 °C (400 °F, gas 6).

Curried Brussels Sprouts with Almonds

Serves 4

20 Brussels sprouts, with
  stems trimmed and slit
5 ml (1 tsp) margarine
40 ml (8 tsp) blanched,
  slivered almonds
10 ml (2 tsp) water
1 small onion, finely
  diced
5 ml (1 tsp) Curry
  Powder (page 162)

Method:
1. Drop the Brussels sprouts into a saucepan containing 2 cm (3/4 inch) boiling water and boil rapidly for about 5 minutes, or until cooked but still firm.
2. Dry the saucepan and return to heat.
3. Melt margarine in saucepan, add almonds and toss until lightly brown; remove from pan.
4. Add 10 ml (2 tsp) water, onion and Curry Powder and stir until onions are lightly cooked.
5. Return sprouts and almonds to saucepan, toss to mix, and serve.

Nutritional data per serve: 312 kJ (75 cal), CHO 3 g, Protein 5 g, Fat 5 g.

Preparation time: 10 minutes. Cooking equipment: saucepan.

Sweet Potato Patties

Serves 4

500 g (1 lb) sweet
  potatoes (yams)
white pepper to taste
good pinch of ground
  cardamom
good pinch ground
  turmeric
2.5 ml (½ tsp) finely
  chopped or minced
  fresh ginger
10 ml (2 tsp) chopped
  parsley
40 ml (8 tsp) snipped
  chives
30 g (1 oz, ½ cup) sesame
  seeds

Method:

1. Peel sweet potatoes (yams) and cut into pieces.
2. Place in saucepan with 250 – 450 ml (8 fl oz – 3/4 pint, 1 – 2 cups) water (or steam or microwave) and the cardamom, and cook until tender.
3. Drain, remove the cardamom and mash the potatoes.
4. Add the other spices, ginger, parsley and chives. Cover and cool (about 1 hour).
5. Shape into patties (four large or eight small).
6. Coat with sesame seeds.
7. Place on baking sheet and bake in a preheated oven for about 30 minutes or until sesame seeds are toasted and patties are heated through.

To vary: replace sesame seeds with wheatgerm.

Nutritional data per serve: 699 kJ (167 cal), CHO 29 g, Protein 7 g, Fat 2 g.

Preparation time: 2 hours. Cooking equipment: medium saucepan, baking sheet. Oven temperature: 200 °C (400 °F, gas 6).

Mushroom and Pecan Rice

Serves 4

125 ml (4 fl oz, ½ cup)
  Chicken Stock (page
  72) or 1 stock cube in
  125 ml (4 fl oz, ½ cup)
  water
6 mushrooms, sliced
4 spring onions
  (shallots), cut into
  12 mm (½ inch) lengths
40 ml (8 tsp) chopped
  pecan nuts
300 g (10 oz, 2 cups)
  cooked brown rice

This filling dish has the complex carbohydrate we need and is wonderfully quick to prepare. Try using walnuts or pine nuts instead of pecan nuts. If you use spring onions (shallots) in place of the onions, add a tablespoon of chopped parsley too.

Method:
1. Heat chicken stock in large pan or wok.
2. Cook mushrooms and onions in stock for 3 – 4 minutes.
3. Add nuts and rice and toss while heating through.
4. Serve hot or chill and serve cold.

Nutritional data per serve: 767 kJ (183 cal), CHO 31 g, Protein 4 g, Fat 5 g.

Preparation time: 15 minutes. Cooking equipment: large pan or wok.

Mushroom Stroganoff

Serves 4

40 ml (8 tsp) water

2 onions, sliced

1 red or green pepper
(capsicum), diced

16 – 20 medium button
mushrooms, sliced

3 spring onions
(shallots), chopped

10 ml (2 tsp) paprika

250 ml (8 fl oz, 1 cup)
low-fat plain yoghurt

garnish: chopped parsley

Serve this dish with brown rice, noodles or beancurd, or use it as a topping for jacket potatoes. It makes an excellent piquant sauce for grilled meats or fillets of chicken and fish.

Method:

1. In the frying pan, bring the water to a simmer and add the onion, red or green pepper (capsicum) and the mushrooms. Simmer gently for 5 minutes.
2. Add spring onions (shallots) and paprika and simmer gently, stirring occasionally, for a further 5 minutes, or microwave for a further 2 minutes on High. Remove from heat.
3. Place yoghurt in a bowl and gradually fold in mushroom mixture. Do not reheat as yoghurt will curdle. Garnish.

Nutritional data per serve: 249 kJ (59 cal), CHO 8 g, Protein 6 g, Fat 1g.

Preparation time: 15 minutes. Cooking equipment: frying pan.

Curried Potatoes and Cauliflower

Serves 4

5 – 10 ml (1 – 2 tsp)
Curry Powder (page
162) according to taste

2 medium potatoes,
scrubbed and diced

½ cauliflower, separated
into florets

1 bay leaf

250 ml (8 fl oz, 1 cup)
boiling water

garnish: chopped parsley

The flavour of curried food improves with standing, so this dish can be prepared 24 hours in advance and stored, well covered in the refrigerator. Reheat before serving.

Method:

1. Dry-fry the Curry Powder in the base of large saucepan for 1 minute, stirring constantly.
2. Add all the other ingredients.
3. Cover saucepan and leave to simmer gently for 20 minutes, or until vegetables are tender and the water absorbed. Remove bay leaf. Serve hot, garnished with parsley.

Nutritional data per serve: 218 kJ, (52 cal), CHO 9 g, Protein 3 g, Fat trace.

Preparation time: 30 minutes. Cooking equipment: saucepan.

Courgette (Zucchini, Baby Marrow) and Tomato Bake

Serves 4

10 ml (2 tsp) margarine
  or oil
1 round of coarse-
  textured bread
2 medium courgettes
  (zucchini, baby
  marrows), cut in half,
  crossways, and then
  into strips
3 tomatoes, sliced
4 spring onions
  (shallots), chopped
10 ml (2 tsp) fresh herbs,
  chopped, or 5 ml (1 tsp)
  dried mixed
pinch of salt (optional)
pinch of pepper
½ medium onion, very
  finely sliced
40 ml (8 tsp) sesame
  seeds
Sauce:
20 ml (4 tsp) tahini paste
juice of ½ lemon
good pinch of finely
  chopped or minced
  fresh ginger
1.5 ml (¼ tsp) prepared
  mustard
water to blend to a thin
  paste

Method:

1. Spread margarine or oil over casserole.
2. Place bread in this. Push into corners without breaking it, and leave excess hanging out.
3. Place half of the courgettes (zucchini, baby marrows) in the bottom.
4. Cover with the sliced tomato.
5. Sprinkle spring onions (shallots), herbs, salt and pepper over.
6. Place the remainder of the courgettes (zucchini, baby marrows) over this, then finely sliced onion.
7. Blend sauce ingredients.
8. Pour mixture over vegetables.
9. Sprinkle with sesame seeds.
10. Fold edges of bread in around the edge of the casserole to form a crust around the edge.
11. Bake in a preheated oven for 40 – 45 minutes or until the bread is brown and crusty, and the courgettes (zucchini, baby marrows) are tender.

Nutritional data per serve: 633 kJ (151 cal), CHO 21 g, Protein 7 g, Fat 4 g.

Preparation time: 15 minutes. Cooking equipment: shallow casserole. Oven temperature: 200 °C (400 °F, gas 6).

Aubergine (Eggplant, Brinjal) Neapolitan

Serves 4

1 large or 2 small
    aubergines (eggplants,
    brinjals) peeled and
    thinly sliced
4 large tomatoes, sliced
2 onions, sliced
2.5 ml (½ tsp) mixed
    dried herbs
ground black pepper to
    taste
1 garlic clove, crushed
250 ml (8 fl oz, 1 cup)
    tomato juice or purée

Method:

1. Layer vegetables in casserole.
2. Sprinkle with herbs, pepper and garlic and pour tomato juice or purée over.
3. Bake in a preheated oven, uncovered, for 45 minutes.

Nutritional data per serve: 258 kJ (62 cal), CHO 11 g, Protein 4 g, Fat trace.

Preparation time: 1 hour. Cooking equipment: deep casserole. Oven temperature: 180 °C (350 °F, gas 4).

Vegetables en Brochette

Serves 4

16 cherry tomatoes
16 pearl onions, peeled
    (or small pieces of
    onion)
16 button mushrooms,
    stalks trimmed
1 medium green pepper
    (capsicum), cut into
    squares
40 ml (8 tsp) lemon juice
10 ml (2 tsp) soy sauce

When you prepare this dish, allow two tomatoes, two onions, two mushrooms and two or three pieces of green pepper (capsicum) per skewer. Serve it with brown rice or on a bed of cracked wheat and you have the basis of a delectable meal.

Method:

1. Thread vegetables evenly along skewers, leaving about 2.5 cm (1 inch) of skewer free at each end.
2. Mix lemon juice and soy sauce and brush mixture over vegetables.
3. Grill for about 5 minutes on each side until vegetables are tender. During grilling, brush with lemon juice and soy sauce mixture at intervals to prevent drying.
4. Serve hot.

Nutritional data per serve: 139 kJ (33 cal), CHO 5 g, Protein 3 g, Fat trace.

Preparation time: 20 minutes. Cooking equipment: eight 18 cm (7 inch) skewers.

Orange-Glazed Parsnips

Serves 4

2 medium parsnips,
   scrubbed and sliced
5 ml (1 tsp) grated
   orange rind
125 ml (4 fl oz, ½ cup)
   orange juice
10 ml (2 tsp) margarine

Carrots cooked this way are splendid too.

Method:

1. Drop parsnips into boiling water and cook until almost tender (about 5 minutes), or microwave, covered with 40 ml (8 tsp) water for 3 minutes until almost tender.
2. Drain, add orange rind, juice and margarine to parsnips.
3. Bring to the boil and cook for a further 3 minutes, or microwave, covered, on High for a further 2 minutes.
4. Lift out parsnips and keep warm.
5. Return saucepan to heat and simmer orange sauce to allow it to reduce and thicken.
6. Once sauce has thickened, pour over parsnips, reheat quickly and serve.

Nutritional data per serve: 246 kJ (59 cal), CHO 8 g, Protein 1 g, Fat 2 g.

Preparation time: 15 minutes. Cooking equipment: saucepan.

Vegeballs

Serves 4

10 ml (2 tsp) margarine
12 small white or pearl
   onions
12 button mushrooms (or
   canned champignons)
12 cherry tomatoes
coarsely ground black
   pepper

Method:

1. Melt margarine in pan or wok.
2. Add onions and toss gently for 3 – 4 minutes until beginning to soften.
3. Add mushrooms and continue tossing until they darken evenly.
4. Add tomatoes and toss very gently until they are heated through.
5. Sprinkle with black pepper.

To vary: substitute small white or pearl onions with 2 cm (3/4 inch) lengths of spring onions (shallots).

Nutritional data per serve: 155 kJ (37 cal), CHO 3 g, Protein 2 g, Fat 2 g

Preparation time: 15 minutes. Cooking equipment: large frying pan or wok.

Sweet and Sour Red Cabbage

Serves 4

500 g (1 lb) red cabbage,
    shredded
1 onion, chopped
1 cooking apple, peeled,
    cored and chopped
1 garlic clove, crushed
20 ml (4 tsp) vinegar
5 ml (1 tsp) caraway seeds
pepper to taste
60 ml (2 fl oz, ¼ cup)
    water

This makes a wonderful companion dish to rice, noodles or potato. Add a small portion of grilled fish or meat and you have the basis for a well-balanced meal.

Method:

1. Place cabbage, onion, apple, garlic, vinegar, caraway seeds and pepper in a saucepan or microwave-proof bowl.
2. Cook over a low heat for 5 minutes, stirring frequently or microwave on High for 3 minutes.
3. Add the water, bring to the boil and simmer for 10 minutes or microwave on High for a further 5 minutes.
4. Arrange the cabbage on a hot serving dish, sprinkle with parsley and serve.

Nutritional data per serve: 204 kJ (49 cal), CHO 8 g, Protein 3 g, Fat trace.
Preparation time: 30 minutes. Cooking equipment: saucepan or microwave-proof bowl.

Crunchy Peasant Rice

Serves 4

½ bunch spinach
20 ml (4 tsp) water
1 small onion, chopped
300 g (10 oz, 2 cups)
    cooked brown rice
15 ml (3 tsp) soy sauce
40 ml (8 tsp) chopped
    Brazil nuts

Almonds or pine nuts are as good in this dish as Brazil nuts.

Method:

1. Wash spinach thoroughly and cook without any additional water in a large saucepan, or microwave for about 2 minutes.
2. Drain well and chop coarsely.
3. Heat large frying pan, add 20 ml (4 tsp) water and sauté onion until transparent.
4. Toss all ingredients lightly together in pan until heated through.

To store: cover and refrigerate for up to three days. Reheat before serving or serve cold.

Nutritional data per serve: 602 kJ (146 cal), CHO 17 g, Protein 6 g, Fat 6 g.
Preparation time: 10 minutes. Cooking equipment: large saucepan or microwave dish, large frying pan.

Vegetables Julienne

Serves 4

1 small courgette
(zucchini, baby
marrow)
2 medium carrots
8 French beans
1 celery stick
½ green pepper
(capsicum)
4 spring onions (shallots)
350 ml (12 fl oz,
1 ½ cups) water
1 chicken stock cube

Prepare the vegetables neatly using a small, sharp knife. Cook them quickly and serve them right away.

Method:

1. Trim top from courgette (zucchini, baby marrow). Cut in half widthways, then lengthways and, finally, into julienne strips.
2. Peel carrots, cut as for courgette (zucchini, baby marrow). Top and tail beans. Cut each in half widthways, then in half lengthways.
3. Cut celery into lengths, then into strips. Cut pepper (capsicum) into strips, removing any pith and seeds.
4. Trim spring onions (shallots), cut into lengths, then each length in half.
5. Add water and stock cube to saucepan, bring to the boil.
6. Add carrots, cook for 2 – 3 minutes, then beans, celery and courgette (zucchini) and cook a further minute.
7. Lastly, add pepper (capsicum) and spring onions (shallots) and cook a further minute.
8. Drain, then gently lift vegetables from water, using tongs or a slotted spoon to avoid breaking strips.

Nutritional data per serve: 146 kJ (35 cal), CHO 6 g, Protein 2 g, Fat trace.
Preparation time: 20 minutes. Cooking equipment: saucepan.

Hot Shredded Beetroot

Serves 4

2 medium beetroot
10 ml (2 tsp) margarine
6 spring onions
(shallots), chopped
5 ml (1 tsp) black pepper
pinch of salt (optional)

Beetroot has a sweetness that adds contrast to a meal.

Method:

1. Top and tail beets, peel and grate.
2. Heat margarine in a frying pan over medium-high heat and add beetroot, spring onions (shallots), black pepper and salt.
3. Sauté gently, turning from time to time, for about 10 minutes or until cooked through.

Nutritional data per serve: 222 kJ (53 cal), CHO 7 g, Protein 2 g, Fat 2 g.
Preparation time: 20 minutes. Cooking equipment: frying pan.

Stir-Fried Vegetables

Serves 4

½ Chinese cabbage or
    ½ green cabbage
5 ml (1 tsp) oil
1 small white onion,
    quartered
5 ml (1 tsp) minced fresh
    ginger
100 g (3 ½ oz, ¾ cup)
    broccoli florets
1 small carrot, finely
    sliced
10 – 12 mangetout
    (snow peas)
75 g (2 ½ oz, ¾ cup)
    beanshoots
½ green pepper
    (capsicum), diced
mushrooms, sliced
125 ml (4 fl oz, ½ cup)
    water
1 stock cube
20 ml (4 tsp) soy sauce

Stir-fried vegetables should be crisp and brightly coloured – the result of swift cooking over high heat.

Method:

1. Prepare the Chinese cabbage by cutting off the woody ends of stalks; discard. Cut the stalks into 2.5 cm (1 inch) lengths and shred the leaves. Cut the cabbage leaves into shreds about 5 cm (2 inches) long.
2. Place wok or heavy frying pan over high heat. Coat thinly with the oil. When very hot add fresh ginger and onion. Stir-fry for 2 – 3 minutes.
3. Add remaining vegetables, stir-fry for 2 – 3 minutes more.
4. Dissolve the stock cube in water; add to vegetables.
5. Turn the heat down, add the soy sauce and combine with the vegetables. Cover the wok or pan and simmer vegetables for 3 – 4 minutes. Serve hot.

Nutritional data per serve: 172 kJ (41 cal), CHO 6 g, Protein 4 g, Fat 1 g.

Preparation time: 20 minutes. Cooking equipment: wok or heavy frying pan.

Cracked Wheat

Serves 4

200 g (7 oz / 1 ½ cups)
    cracked wheat
    (burghul or pearled
    wheat)
350 ml (12 fl oz,
    1 ½ cups) Chicken
    Stock (page 72)

In line with the new way to eat, carbohydrate should be central to the meal. Cracked wheat (burghul or pearled wheat) prepared this way is quick and easy. Use it to build a meal just as you would with brown rice or wholemeal noodles.

Method:

1. Wash cracked wheat (burghul) under cold running water.
2. Place in saucepan, pour chicken stock over. Simmer for 10 – 15 minutes until tender.

Nutritional data per serve: 593 kJ (139 cal), CHO 26 g, Protein 6 g, Fat 1 g.
Preparation time: 15 minutes. Cooking equipment: saucepan.

Salads

All the salad ideas we give here are simple but show you that, with a little inspiration, a salad can add something special to a meal. All these recipes will serve four.

Asparagus and Green Bean Salad

Trim eight spears of fresh asparagus and cut them into 7.5 cm (3 inch) lengths. Top, tail and halve twelve green beans. Boil, steam or microwave them until just tender, then drop them into icy water to cool them quickly: this helps retain their crispness and colour. Drain. Wash and dry a round lettuce, tear it into pieces and line a salad bowl. Combine the asparagus, beans and sixteen cherry tomatoes and place them in the salad bowl. Pour over 60 ml (2 fl oz, 1/4 cup) Italian Dressing (page 158) and sprinkle 40 ml (8 tsp) toasted sesame seeds over.

Ginger Carrots

Slice two medium carrots into long strips with a potato peeler. Add a little peeled and finely chopped fresh ginger and then pour 125 ml (4 fl oz, 1/2 cup) white wine vinegar over. Refrigerate for 2 hours before serving. You can add thinly sliced cucumber if you like.

Tomato and Onion

Slice three firm, ripe tomatoes and a white onion. Pour 125 ml (4 fl oz, 1/2 cup) brown vinegar over. Add freshly ground black pepper. Refrigerate for at least 30 minutes before serving.

Orange and Cucumber Salad

Peel and slice two oranges, removing all pith. Slice half a cucumber and a small onion. Break the onion into separate rings. Mix and sprinkle them with 20 ml (4 tsp) chopped parsley and, finally, pour over one quantity of Creamy Orange Dressing (page 159). Chill well before serving.

Mushroom Salad

Slice ten medium mushrooms into a bowl. Add 90 g (3 oz, 1 cup) beanshoots (bean sprouts), 60 g (2 oz, 1/2 cup) each of celery and red pepper (capsicum), cut into matchsticks, and two chopped spring onions (shallots). Toss with 1/2 quantity of Orange and Soy Dressing (page 158) or Herby Tomato Dressing (page 159) and chill well.

Avocado, Spinach and Tofu Salad

Wash a bunch of spinach, remove the stalks and tear the leaves into bite-sized pieces. Place spinach in a bowl and add a sliced medium avocado, eight pitted and quartered black olives and 250 g (8 oz) firm tofu (soybean curd) cut into small cubes. Make a dressing of 10 ml (2 tsp) olive oil, 20 ml (4 tsp) lemon juice and a crushed garlic clove; pour it over the salad and toss lightly. Chill.

Broccoli, Beanshoots (Bean Sprouts) and Mangetout (Snow Peas) with Lemon

Blanch 300 g (10 oz, 2 cups) broccoli florets by cooking them in boiling water or steaming them for 3 minutes. Plunge quickly under cold water to cool. Steam 150 g (5 oz) mangetout (snow peas) for 1 – 2 minutes; cool quickly under cold water. Rinse 90 g (3 oz, 1 cup) beanshoots (bean sprouts) and combine them with the broccoli and mangetout (snow peas) in a bowl. Pour over a dressing of 40 ml (8 tsp) lemon juice, 2.5 ml (½ tsp) coarsely ground black pepper and 10 ml (2 tsp) oil. Serve chilled.

Fruity Noodle Salad

Serves 4

410 g (14 oz, 2 ½ cups)
  cooked noodles
90 g (3 oz, ½ cup)
  sultanas
1 celery stick, diced
3 spring onions
  (shallots), chopped
1 green apple, cored and
  diced
4 dried apricots, chopped
4 dried peaches, chopped
60 g (2 oz, ⅓ cup) pine
  nuts
Dressing:
125 ml (4 fl oz, ½ cup)
  orange juice
1 garlic clove, crushed
5 ml (1 tsp) minced fresh
  ginger
5 ml (1 tsp) lemon juice
1 sweetener equivalent to
  10 ml (2 tsp) sugar

Method:

1. Combine all ingredients, except the pine nuts, in salad bowl.
2. Toast pine nuts in a moderate oven for 5 – 8 minutes until golden brown. Cool and then add to other ingredients.
3. Combine the dressing ingredients in a screw-top jar, shake well and pour over salad.
4. Toss salad, cover and refrigerate for several hours before serving.

To store: keep in airtight container in refrigerator for up to three days.

Nutritional data per serve: 1368 kJ (327 cal), CHO 56 g, Protein 9 g, Fat 8 g.

Preparation time: 15 minutes. Cooking equipment: baking sheet. Oven temperature: 180 °C (350 °F, gas 4).

Foreground: Turkey with Strawberry and Peppercorn Sauce with Orange-glazed Parsnips, steamed mangetout (snow peas) and asparagus. Front left Gazpacho. Then Christmas Pudding smothered in Brandy Sauce and beribboned Christmas Cake.

Curried Pasta Salad

Serves 4

200 g (7 oz, 1 ½ cups)
   uncooked shell pasta
   (noodles)
60 g (2 oz, ½ cup) diced
   celery
4 spring onions
   (shallots), chopped
40 ml (8 tsp) sultanas
½ green pepper
   (capsicum), diced
40 ml (8 tsp) chopped
   parsley
90 g (3 oz, ½ cup)
   sweetcorn kernels
Dressing:
½ quantity Curry
   Dressing (page 160)

Method:

1. Cook pasta (noodles) in boiling water for 10 – 12 minutes until *al dente* (tender), drain and then run cold water over to cool them.
2. Combine pasta (noodles), celery, spring onions (shallots), sultanas, pepper (capsicum), parsley and sweetcorn.
3. Toss in Curry Dressing.
4. Refrigerate for 1 hour before serving.

To store: keep in airtight container in refrigerator and store for up to two days.

Nutritional data per serve: 556 kJ (133 cal), CHO 26 g, Protein 5 g, Fat 1 g.

Preparation time: 1¼ hours. Cooking equipment: saucepan.

Spinach Valentino

Serves 4

1 bunch spinach
4 mushrooms, sliced
2 spring onions
   (shallots), sliced
2 eggs, hard-boiled
1 quantity Orange
   and Soy Dressing
   (page 158)

Method:

1. Wash spinach thoroughly and shake gently to remove excess water. Remove the stalks and tear into bite-sized pieces.
2. Combine spinach, mushrooms, spring onions (shallots) and sliced eggs and toss in dressing.
3. Chill before serving.

Nutritional data per serve: 266 kJ (63 cal), CHO 2 g, Protein 5 g, Fat 4 g.

Preparation time: 5 minutes.

Foreground: Jacket Potato with Yoghurt and Chives beside Stuffed Tomato served with Fish and Green Champagne Sauce. Centre left Bread and Butter Custard.

New Potato Salad

Serves 4

---

16 small new potatoes
45 ml (9 tsp) chopped
  fresh mint
40 ml (8 tsp) snipped
  fresh chives or chopped
  spring onions (shallots)
200 g (7 oz) low-fat plain
  yoghurt
2.5 ml (½ tsp) minced
  fresh ginger
2.5 ml (½ tsp) minced
  garlic
2.5 ml (½ tsp) prepared
  mild mustard
5 ml (1 tsp) lemon juice

Method:

1. Scrub potatoes if necessary, but do not peel.
2. Boil, steam or microwave the potatoes until tender. Drain and cool.
3. Place in serving bowl and add mint and chives or spring onions (shallots).
4. In a small mixing bowl combine yoghurt, ginger, garlic, mustard and lemon juice. Mix well.
5. Pour over potatoes; mix well. Cover and refrigerate until ready to serve.

Nutritional data per serve: 343 kJ (82 cal), CHO 14 g, Protein 5 g, Fat 1 g.

Preparation time: 2¾ hours including cooling time. Cooking equipment: medium saucepan.

Tabbouleh

Serves 4

---

75 g (2½ oz, ½ cup)
  cracked wheat
  (burghul)
2 large ripe tomatoes,
  skinned and finely
  chopped
1 small onion, finely
  chopped
60 g (2 oz, 1 cup)
  chopped parsley
ground black pepper
10 ml (2 tsp) olive oil
40 ml (8 tsp) lemon juice
20 ml (4 tsp) finely
  chopped mint

Method:

1. Place cracked wheat (burghul) in a deep bowl, cover with boiling water and allow to stand for 2 hours.
2. Drain well by squeezing in a clean muslin cloth or tea-towel and return to bowl.
3. Add the tomatoes, onion, parsley, pepper, oil, lemon juice and mint.
4. Combine well and chill for 1 hour before serving.

Nutritional data per serve: 470 kJ (112 cal), CHO 17 g, Protein 4 g, Fat 3 g.

Preparation time: soaking time 2 hours, preparation 15 minutes, chilling time 1 hour.

Curried Sweet Potato and Banana Salad

Serves 4

3 medium sweet potatoes
   (yams), peeled
2 medium bananas
20 ml (4 tsp) lemon juice
2 spring onions
   (shallots), chopped
1 quantity Curry
   Dressing (page 160)

Method:
1. Cut the sweet potatoes (yams) into 2 cm (3/4 inch) cubes.
2. Place in a large saucepan and barely cover with cold water. Bring to the boil, reduce heat and simmer for 10 – 12 minutes, or until potato (yam) is cooked through but still holds its shape. Alternatively, microwave on High for 5 – 6 minutes.
3. Meanwhile, slice banana and toss in lemon juice.
4. Drain the cooked potato (yam) and allow to cool.
5. In a salad bowl place the potato (yam), banana, spring onions (shallots) and dressing and toss gently to combine.

Nutritional data per serve: 524 kJ (125 cal), CHO 26 g, Protein 4 g, Fat 1 g.

Preparation time: 20 minutes. Cooking equipment: large saucepan.

Tangy Potato Salad

Serves 4

3 medium potatoes
4 spring onions
   (shallots), chopped
3 eggs, hard-boiled and
   sliced
125 ml (4 fl oz, ½ cup)
   low-fat plain yoghurt
2.5 ml (½ tsp) black
   pepper coarsely ground
10 ml (2 tsp) Curry
   Powder (page 162)
4 lettuce cups

This salad is best when made in advance as the flavour develops during refrigeration.

Method:
1. Peel potatoes.
2. Cook until slightly soft, but do not over-cook as potato will not hold its shape. Drain.
3. Cut potato into cubes and mix with spring onions (shallots).
4. Add eggs.
5. Combine yoghurt, pepper and Curry Powder. Spoon over the potato mixture and toss gently.
6. Store in airtight container in refrigerator until required.
7. Serve in lettuce cups.

To store: cover and refrigerate for up to two days.

Nutritional data per serve: 550 kJ (131 cal), CHO 14 g, Protein 9 g, Fat 4 g.

Preparation time: 30 minutes. Cooking equipment: saucepan.

Coleslaw

Serves 4

1/4 medium cabbage,
  finely shredded
1 small onion, grated
1 small green pepper
  (capsicum), chopped
1 celery stick, chopped
45 g (1½ oz, ⅓ cup) grated
  carrot
ground black pepper
½ quantity Creamy
  Yoghurt Dressing
  (page 158)

Once you have added the dressing, coleslaw should not be stored. However, you can prepare the vegetables in advance and store them in the refrigerator: add the dressing just before serving.

Method:

Toss all ingredients in a large bowl; chill until ready to serve.

To vary: add 60 g (2 oz, 1/3 cup) chopped pineapple and 40 ml (8 tsp) sultanas. Substitute Creamy Yoghurt Dressing for commercial low oil coleslaw dressing.

To store: cover and refrigerate for no more than a day.

Nutritional data per serve: 122 kJ (29 cal), CHO 5 g, Protein 2 g, Fat trace.

Broad Bean and Smoked Salmon Salad

Serves 4

---

250 g (8 oz) shelled
  broad beans, frozen or
  fresh
90 g (3 oz) smoked
  salmon, thinly sliced
12 cherry tomatoes
1 small white onion,
  thinly sliced
40 ml (8 tsp) lemon juice
10 ml (2 tsp) olive oil
10 ml (2 tsp) capers,
  drained
10 ml (2 tsp) chopped
  fresh parsley

Method:

1. Cook broad beans until they are soft but still retain their shape.
2. Combine broad beans, smoked salmon, cherry tomatoes and white onion in a bowl.
3. Blend all the other ingredients in a screw-top jar and pour over the salad.
4. Chill and serve.

Nutritional data per serve: 414 kJ (99 cal), CHO 12 g, Protein 0 g, Fat 4 g.

Preparation time: 20 minutes. Cooking equipment: saucepan.

Fettucine Salmon Salad

Serves 4

1 litre (1 ¾ pints) water
250 g (8 oz) fresh
   spinach fettuccine
6 spring onions (shallots)
½ celery stick
½ pepper (capsicum)
1 tomato
½ courgette (zucchini,
   baby marrow)
1/2 avocado
200 g (7 oz) canned red
   (pink) salmon
125 g (4 oz, 1 cup) grated
   carrot
Dressing:
40 ml (8 tsp) chopped
   mint
juice of ½ lemon
juice of 1 orange
10 ml (2 tsp) olive oil
10 ml (2 tsp) soy sauce

Method:

1. Heat water until boiling.
2. Add fettuccine and cook until *al dente* (tender).
3. Drain, rinse and cool.
4. Chop spring onions (shallots), celery, pepper (capsicum) and tomato.
5. Cut courgette (zucchini, baby marrow) into fine strips.
6. Peel avocado, discard stone and chop roughly.
7. Drain salmon; remove bones and skin.
8. Combine pasta with all other ingredients and mix gently.
9. Mix dressing ingredients and pour over. Serve.

Nutritional data per serve: 1189 kJ (284 cal), CHO 25 g, Protein 16 g, Fat 13 g.

Preparation time: 45 minutes. Cooking equipment: saucepan.

Raita

Serves 4

¼ cucumber
pinch of salt
1 medium tomato
1 small onion
200 g (7 oz) low-fat plain
   yoghurt
pepper
good pinch of minced
   garlic
3 – 4 drops of Tabasco

Method:

1. Peel and chop the cucumber. Sprinkle with salt. Place in sieve over bowl and allow to drain for 30 minutes.
2. Chop tomato and place in another bowl.
3. Slice onion very finely.
4. Mix tomato, onion and cucumber.
5. Mix yoghurt, pepper, garlic and Tabasco.
6. Pour yoghurt mixture over vegetables, mix well and refrigerate for an hour.

Nutritional data per serve: 174 kJ (42 cal), CHO 6 g, Protein 3 g, Fat 1 g.

Preparation time: 2 hours.

Crunchy Rice Salad

Serves 4

---

300 g (10 oz, 2 cups)
cooked brown rice
½ green pepper
(capsicum), chopped
½ red pepper (capsicum),
chopped
4 spring onions
(shallots), sliced
4 radishes, finely sliced
1 celery stick, finely
sliced
30 g (1 oz, ¼ cup)
unsalted, roasted
peanuts
60 g (2 oz, ½ cup) canned
water chestnuts,
drained and sliced
60 g (2 oz, ½ cup) green
beans, lightly cooked
20 ml (4 tsp) soy sauce
5 ml (1 tsp) sugar
40 ml (8 tsp) chopped
parsley
45 g (1½ oz, ½ cup)
beanshoots (bean
sprouts)
pinch of salt (optional)

Method:

1. Combine all ingredients.
2. Chill.
3. Serve, garnished with chopped spring onions (shallots) and radish slices.

Nutritional data per serve: 901 kJ (215 cal), CHO 35 g, Protein 7 g, Fat 5 g.

Preparation time: 30 minutes.

Tossed Salad

Serves 4

---

60 ml (2 fl oz, ¼ cup)
Italian Dressing (page
158) or commercial
low-oil dressing

Use your imagination in creating tossed salads. For instance, consider blanched green beans, young courgettes (zucchini, baby marrows), broccoli florets and cauliflower. You can combine alfalfa sprouts, mushrooms, mangetout (snow peas), carrot and celery with the more traditional ingredients such as various kinds of lettuce, peppers (capsicum), cucumber and tomatoes. Avocado adds a certain richness, but also fat.

Sauces, Dressings and Marinades

SAUCES

White Sauce

Makes about 450 ml
(¾ pint, 2 cups)

450 ml (¾ pint, 2 cups)
  skimmed milk
1 onion, cut in half
1 small carrot, roughly
  chopped
1 celery stick, roughly
  chopped
6 peppercorns
40 ml (8 tsp) cornflour
  (cornstarch)

Method:

1. Pour milk into saucepan. Add chopped vegetables and peppercorns.
2. Bring mixture to the boil. Immediately reduce heat and simmer for 15 minutes.
3. Strain milk into a bowl. Discard vegetables and peppercorns.
4. In a separate bowl, mix cornflour (cornstarch) with 40 – 60 ml (8 – 12 tsp) of the warm milk. Stir to make a smooth paste.
5. Gradually add remaining milk to the paste, stirring all the time.
6. Return sauce to the saucepan. Bring to the boil, stirring constantly. Reduce heat and simmer gently for 2 minutes, stirring until sauce thickens.
7. Use as required in recipes.

Nutritional data per total quantity: 1036 kJ (247 cal), CHO 40 g, Protein 20 g, Fat 1 g.

Preparation time: 20 minutes. Cooking equipment: medium saucepan.

Green Champagne Sauce

Makes about 250 ml
(8 fl oz, 1 cup)

3 kiwi fruit, peeled and
  puréed
60 g (2 oz, ½ cup) white
  seedless grapes, halved
125 ml (4 fl oz, ½ cup)
  champagne

Simple, sophisticated and superb, especially with fish.

Method:

1. Place kiwi fruit in saucepan. Add grapes and champagne.
2. Heat gently but do not boil. Serve immediately.

Nutritional data per total quantity: 1210 kJ (289 cal), CHO 46 g, Protein 5 g, Fat 1 g.

Preparation time: 10 minutes. Cooking equipment: small-medium saucepan.

Cheese Sauce

Makes about 450 ml
(¾ pint, 2 cups)

250 g (8 oz) cottage or
* ricotta cheese*
60 g (2 oz, ½ cup) grated
* low-fat hard cheese*
125 ml (4 fl oz, ½ cup)
* skimmed milk*
20 ml (4 tsp) cornflour
* (cornstarch)*
20 ml (4 tsp) extra
* skimmed milk*

This versatile and popular sauce works well with any number of savoury dishes. It is especially delicious with fish, vegetables or pasta. If you'd like a little more 'bite' to the sauce, add 2.5 ml (1/2 tsp) prepared English mustard and a pinch of cayenne pepper.

Method:

1. Using a food processor or electric blender, blend cottage or ricotta cheese and skimmed milk until smooth. Add the grated hard cheese.
2. In a saucepan, gently warm the cheese mixture, stirring constantly, until the grated cheese melts.
3. In a cup, blend the cornflour (cornstarch) with the extra 20 ml (4 tsp) milk to make a smooth paste. Add to saucepan and stir into sauce.
4. Stirring constantly, bring sauce to the boil. Immediately reduce heat and simmer gently for 2 minutes, stirring constantly.

Nutritional data per total quantity: 2084 kJ (498 cal), CHO 21 g, Protein 66 g, Fat 18 g.

Preparation time: 10 minutes. Cooking equipment: medium saucepan, food processor or blender.

Saté (Peanut) Sauce

Makes about 450 ml
(¾ pint, 2 cups).

20 ml (4 tsp) water
1 small onion, grated
1 garlic clove, crushed
2.5 – 5 ml (½ – 1 tsp)
* chilli powder*
170 g (6 oz, ¾ cup)
* crunchy peanut butter*
* (preferably low-salt)*
20 ml (4 tsp) soy sauce
20 ml (4 tsp) lemon juice
275 ml (9 fl oz, 1¼ cups)
* water*

Method:

1. In a frying pan, bring water to the boil. Add onion and garlic and cook gently until soft.
2. Add chilli powder, stir and cook for 1 minute over medium heat.
3. Add peanut butter and stir well. Add soy sauce, lemon juice and water and mix well. Bring mixture to the boil, stirring constantly. Reduce heat and simmer gently for 1 minute.

Nutritional data per total quantity: 1965 kJ (477 cal), CHO 9 g, Protein 14 g, Fat 85 g.

Preparation time: 20 minutes. Cooking equipment: frying pan.

Fresh Vegetable Sauce

Makes about 1 litre
(1 ¾ pints, 4 cups)

1 apple, peeled and
   grated
1 medium carrot, grated
1 medium courgette
   (zucchini, baby
   marrow), grated
¼ medium green pepper
   (capsicum), finely
   chopped
1 small onion, finely
   chopped
2 medium tomatoes,
   finely chopped
3 medium mushrooms,
   finely chopped
1 garlic clove, crushed
20 ml (4 tsp) finely
   chopped parsley
2.5 ml (½ tsp) finely
   chopped fresh sage or
   good pinch of dried
2.5 ml (½ tsp) finely
   chopped fresh
   marjoram or good
   pinch of dried
ground black pepper
40 ml (8 tsp) tomato
   paste
125 ml (4 fl oz, ½ cup)
   water

The perfect sauce for any meal in the Italian style.

Method:

Place all ingredients in saucepan, bring to the boil and simmer for 20 minutes. Alternatively, place the ingredients in a microwave-proof bowl and microwave on High for 10 minutes.

Nutritional data per total quantity: 795 kJ (193 cal), CHO 40 g, Protein 17 g, Fat 1 g.

Preparation time: 30 minutes. Cooking equipment: medium saucepan.

Black Bean Sauce

Makes about 125 ml (4 fl oz, 1/2 cup)

60 g (2 oz) cooked black
    beans
1 garlic clove, crushed
2.5 ml (½ tsp) finely
    chopped or minced
    fresh ginger (optional)
20 ml (4 tsp) brandy or
    dry sherry
60 ml (2 fl oz, ¼ cup)
    water
10 ml (2 tsp) soy sauce

Delicious with finely sliced sautéed steak, chicken fillets or fish.

Method:

1. Drain beans thoroughly and mash with garlic, ginger and brandy or sherry.
2. Place in saucepan with water and soy sauce.
3. Bring to the boil, reduce heat and simmer for 2 minutes.

Nutritional data per total quantity: 767 kJ (183 cal), CHO 16 g, Protein 15 g, Fat 8 g.

Preparation time: 7 minutes. Cooking equipment: small saucepan.

Ratatouille Sauce

Serves 4

1 small green pepper
    (capsicum), diced
1 small aubergine
    (brinjal, eggplant),
    peeled and diced
2 small courgettes
    (zucchini, baby
    marrows), diced
2 medium tomatoes,
    diced, or 16 cherry
    tomatoes
6 medium mushrooms,
    diced
1 large onion, peeled and
    diced
1 garlic clove, crushed
2.5 ml (½ tsp) dried
    oregano
black pepper to taste
60 ml (2 fl oz) water

Ratatouille can be served as a hot vegetable or chilled as a salad. It is also ideal used to surround chicken, veal or fish fillets during cooking.

Method:

Combine all ingredients and cook over low heat for 30 minutes, or microwave on Medium for 15 minutes.

Nutritional data per total quantity: 184 kJ (44 cal), CHO 7 g, Protein 4 g, Fat 1 g.

Preparation time: 45 minutes. Cooking equipment: saucepan.

Tomato and Basil Sauce

Serves 4

10 ml (2 tsp) olive oil
1 medium onion, finely
　chopped
1 garlic clove, crushed
500 g (1 lb) ripe
　tomatoes, peeled,
　seeded and chopped
20 ml (4 tsp) chopped
　fresh basil
2.5 ml (½ tsp) chopped
　fresh oregano
ground black pepper

Method:

1. Heat oil in saucepan, add onion and sauté until translucent.
2. Add garlic and cook for a further 2 minutes.
3. Add tomatoes, herbs and pepper and boil for 8 – 10 minutes.

Microwave: Sauté onion until soft (about 30 seconds). Add garlic and cook on High for a further 1 minute. Add the tomatoes, herbs and pepper, and cook on High for 4 – 6 minutes.

Nutritional data per total quantity: 793 kJ (190 cal), CHO 19 g, Protein 6 g, Fat 10 g.

Preparation time: 20 minutes. Cooking equipment: medium saucepan.

Cherry Sauce

**Makes about 450 ml
(3/4 pint, 2 cups)**

300 g (10 oz, 2 cups)
　fresh ripe cherries,
　stoned
125 ml (4 fl oz, ½ cup)
　Chicken Stock
　(page 72) or 125 ml
　(4 fl oz, ½ cup) water
　and 1 stock cube
5 ml (1 tsp)
　Worcestershire Sauce
20 ml (4 tsp) brandy

Method:

1. Place half the cherries in a saucepan or in a microwave bowl with stock and Worcestershire sauce.
2. Boil for 8 minutes until cherries are soft, or microwave on High for 4 minutes. Purée and return to saucepan or bowl.
3. Add remaining cherries and brandy. Simmer for 2 minutes or microwave on High for 2 minutes and serve.

Nutritional data per total quantity: 804 kJ (192 cal), CHO 48 g, Protein 2 g, Fat 0 g.

Preparation time: 15 minutes. Cooking equipment: saucepan.

Cucumber and Yoghurt Sauce

Makes about 250 ml
(8 fl oz, 1 cup)

½ cucumber, peeled

200 g (7 oz) low-fat plain
yoghurt

5 ml (1 tsp) minced fresh
ginger

2.5 ml (½ tsp) minced
garlic

20 ml (4 tsp) lemon juice

good pinch of freshly
ground black pepper

good pinch of paprika

20 ml (4 tsp) chopped
parsley

4 cardamom pods,
crushed

Use this sauce straight away because it will not keep.

Method:

1. Grate cucumber, drain well and discard liquid.
2. Combine all the ingredients in a bowl and chill well before
   serving.

Nutritional data per total quantity: 514 kJ (123 cal), CHO 16 g, Protein 11 g, Fat 2 g.

Preparation time: 15 minutes.

Strawberry and Peppercorn Sauce

Makes about 450 ml
(¾ pint, 2 cups)

125 ml (4 fl oz, ½ cup)
dry white wine

125 g (4 oz) strawberries,
washed, hulled and
puréed

5 ml (1 tsp) lemon juice

5 ml (1 tsp) brandy

10 ml (2 tsp) green or
pink peppercorns

125 ml (4 fl oz, ½ cup)
canned evaporated,
skimmed milk, chilled

Unusual, but wonderful with grilled or sautéed chicken fillets, fish,
lobster or crab.

Method:

1. Bring wine to the boil and reduce to half by simmering.
2. Add strawberry purée, lemon juice, brandy and peppercorns.
3. Bring back to the boil, simmer 1 minute and set aside to cool.
4. Whip evaporated milk until it is thick. Gradually add the
   strawberry mixture, whipping constantly.
5. Gently reheat the mixture, but do not allow it to boil. Serve
   immediately.

Nutritional data per total quantity: 200 kJ (48 cal), CHO 7g, Protein 5 g, Fat trace.

Preparation time: 15 minutes. Cooking equipment: medium
saucepan.

Sweet and Sour Sauce

Serves 4

1 large onion

8 spring onions (shallots)

2 medium carrots

*1 small red pepper
(capsicum), seeded*

125 g (4 oz) mushrooms

2 celery sticks

1 medium cucumber

10 ml (2 tsp) oil

1 garlic clove, crushed

*5 ml (1 tsp) grated or
minced fresh ginger*

*40 ml (8 tsp) tomato
paste*

*60 ml (2 fl oz, ¼ cup)
white wine vinegar*

*250 ml (8 fl oz, 1 cup)
water*

1 stock cube

*30 ml (6 tsp) cornflour
(cornstarch)*

*60 ml (2 fl oz, ¼ cup) soy
sauce*

20 ml (4 tsp) dry sherry

*410 g (14 oz) canned
unsweetened pineapple
chunks and juice*

This is a wonderfully versatile sauce that is just as good served with boiled brown rice or noodles as it is served with grilled fish, pork or vegetables.

Method:

1. Slice onion, spring onions (shallots), pepper (capsicum), mushrooms and celery into matchsticks.

2. Cut cucumbers into quarters, lengthwise, remove seeds and cut into small pieces of about 12 mm (1/2 inch).

3. Heat oil in a large wok or frying pan over high heat. Add garlic and ginger. Stir-fry for 30 seconds and then add all the other vegetables. Keep heat high and stir-fry for 2 – 3 minutes more until the vegetables are cooked but still crisp and brightly coloured.

4. In a bowl, blend tomato paste, vinegar, water, stock cube, cornflour (cornstarch), soy sauce and sherry.

5. Drain pineapple pieces and add the juice to the tomato paste mixture. Set pineapple aside. Add sauce mixture to the vegetables and stir until sauce boils and thickens.

6. Add the pineapple to the vegetables and cook for another 3 – 5 minutes, until the pineapple is heated through.

To serve: as an accompaniment: serve hot or cold with Grilled Fish (page 89) or Pork, and Vegetables en Brochette (page 138). As a light meal: serve the sauce with boiled brown rice or noodles.

Nutritional data per total quantity: 2163 kJ (517 cal), CHO 87 g, Protein 17 g, Fat 11 g.

Preparation time: 30 minutes. Cooking equipment: wok or frying pan.

DRESSINGS

Italian Dressing

Makes about 125 ml
(4 fl oz, 1/2 cup)

75 ml (2½ fl oz, ½ cup)
  wine vinegar
20 ml (4 tsp) lemon juice
20 ml (4 tsp) chopped
  parsley
10 ml (2 tsp) snipped
  chives
1 garlic clove, crushed
2.5 ml (½ tsp) mustard
  powder
ground black pepper

Method:
Combine the ingredients in a screw-top jar, shake well and refrigerate.

To store: cover and refrigerate for up to one week.

Nutritional data per total quantity: negligible.

Preparation time: 5 minutes.

Creamy Yoghurt Dressing

Makes about 125 ml
(4 fl oz, 1/2 cup)

75 ml (2 ½ fl oz, ⅓ cup)
  low-fat plain yoghurt
40 ml (8 tsp) lemon juice
  or raspberry vinegar
2.5 ml (½ tsp) mustard
  powder
ground black pepper

Method:
Mix all ingredients until smooth. Cover and refrigerate.

To store: cover and refrigerate for up to three days.

Nutritional data per total quantity: 189 kJ (45 cal), CHO 6 g, Protein 4 g, Fat 1 g.

Preparation time: 5 minutes.

Orange and Soy Dressing

Makes about 60 ml
(2 fl oz, 1/4 cup)

60 ml (2 fl oz, ¼ cup)
  unsweetened orange
  juice
10 ml (2 tsp) soy sauce
1 garlic clove, crushed
5 ml (1 tsp) oil (optional)

Method:
1. Combine all ingredients in a screw-top jar.
2. Chill and shake well before use.

Nutritional data per total quantity: 269 kJ (64 cal), CHO 4 g, Protein trace, Fat 5 g.

Preparation time: 5 minutes.

Herby Tomato Dressing

Makes about 250 ml
(8 fl oz, 1 cup)

125 ml (4 fl oz, ½ cup)
  unsweetened tomato
  juice
75 ml (2 ½ fl oz) tomato
  paste
40 ml (8 tsp) low-fat
  plain yoghurt
4 drops Tabasco
1 garlic clove, crushed
20 ml (4 tsp) chopped
  parsley
2.5 ml (½ tsp) chopped
  fresh mixed herbs or
  good portion mixed
  dried herbs

Use herbs such as marjoram, basil or thyme.

Method:
1. Combine tomato juice with tomato paste and add to yoghurt.
2. Add other ingredients and mix.
3. Chill until ready to use.

Nutritional data per total quantity: 411 kJ (98 cal),
CHO 16 g, Protein 8 g, Fat trace.

Preparation time: 8 minutes.

Creamy Orange Dressing

Makes about 175 ml
(6 fl oz, ¾ cup)

60 ml (2 fl oz, ¼ cup)
  unsweetened orange
  juice
10 ml (2 tsp) grated
  orange rind
20 ml (4 tsp) finely
  chopped parsley
10 ml (2 tsp) finely
  snipped chives
125 ml (4 fl oz, ½ cup)
  low-fat plain yoghurt

Method:

Combine all ingredients and chill.

To vary: for a creamy lemon dressing, prepare as above but omit orange juice and rind, replacing them with 40 ml (8 tsp) lemon juice.

To store: cover and refrigerate for up to two days.

Nutritional data per total quantity: 421 kJ (101 cal),
CHO 14 g, Protein 8 g, Fat 2 g.

Preparation time: 5 minutes.

Curry Dressing

Makes about 125 ml
(4 fl oz, 1/2 cup)

---

125 ml (4 fl oz, ½ cup)
low-fat plain yoghurt
10 ml (2 tsp) hot Curry
Powder or Paste
(page 162)
40 ml (8 tsp) chopped
parsley
good pinch of minced
garlic (optional)

Method:

1. Mix all ingredients and adjust flavouring to taste.
2. Chill until ready to use.

Nutritional data per total quantity: 337 kJ (80 cal),
CHO 9 g, Protein 8 g, Fat 2 g.

Preparation time: 5 minutes.

PICKLES AND SEASONINGS

Tomato Relish

Makes about 2 litres
(3½ pints, 8 cups)

---

3 large onions
2.5 kg (5½ lb) ripe
tomatoes, chopped
5 Granny Smith apples,
cored and chopped
750 ml (1¼ pints,
3 cups) vinegar
500 g (1 lb) sultanas
3 cloves garlic, crushed
250 ml (8 fl oz, 1 cup)
fresh orange juice
5 ml (1 tsp) mixed spice
5 ml (1 tsp) whole cloves
5 ml (1 tsp) chilli powder

Method:

1. Place all the ingredients in a large saucepan and bring them to the boil. Turn the heat to low and simmer for 1 hour, stirring frequently. Remove from heat.
2. Pour hot water into clean jars to warm them.
3. Fill jars with hot chutney. Allow them to cool, then seal the jars and store.

To store: keep in sealed jars. Once opened, store in refrigerator.

Nutritional data per total quantity: 8820 kJ (2107 cal),
CHO 503 g, Protein 42 g, Fat 1 g.

Preparation time: 1 ½ hours. Cooking equipment: large saucepan.

Foreground: Corn Chowder, centre left Apple Layer Cake and centre right Meat Loaf with Spicy Barbecue Sauce

Fresh Mango Pickle

**Makes about 250 ml
(8 fl oz, 1 cup)**

1 ripe medium-large
   mango
10 ml (2 tsp) lemon juice
2.5 ml (½ tsp) finely
   chopped or minced
   fresh ginger
20 ml (4 tsp) sultanas

Method:

1. Peel mango. Slice flesh from stone and cut into small pieces. Place in a mixing bowl.
2. Add lemon juice, ginger and sultanas.
3. Spoon into glass or plastic container, cover and refrigerate.

To store: keep in glass or plastic container and refrigerate for up to two days.

Nutritional data per total quantity: 425 kJ (102 cal), CHO 24 g, Protein 2 g, Fat trace.

Preparation time: 15 minutes.

Plum Sauce

**Makes: about 2 litres
(3½ pints, 8 cups)**

2 onions, chopped
250 ml (4 fl oz, 1 cup)
   water
1 kg (2 lb) fresh plums,
   stoned
250 ml (4 fl oz, 1 cup)
   fresh orange juice
10 ml (2 tsp) grated or
   minced fresh ginger
2.5 ml (½ tsp) whole
   cloves
a few peppercorns
pinch of thyme
pinch of oregano
1 bay leaf

Method:

1. Lightly sauté onions in 45 – 60 ml (1/2 – 2 fl oz) of the water for 2 minutes.
2. Add the rest of the ingredients and cook over low heat, stirring regularly.
3. Simmer, uncovered, for at least 1 hour until the mixture thickens.
4. Pour into clean warmed jars, allow to cool and then seal.

To store: keep in sealed jars in refrigerator.

*Nutritional data per total quantity: 2238 kJ (545 cal),
CHO 124 g, Protein 12 g, Fat 1 g.*

Preparation time: 1½ hours. Cooking equipment: large saucepan.

Foreground: Pikelets and Fresh Strawberry Conserve, centre Carrot Cake with a basket of Herby Corn Muffins, and Wholemeal Scones at top.

Curry Paste

Makes 175 ml
(6 fl oz, $^3/_4$ cup)

20 ml (4 tsp) minced or
   grated fresh ginger
40 ml (8 tsp) ground
   coriander
20 ml (4 tsp) ground
   cinnamon
10 ml (2 tsp) chilli
   powder
20 ml (4 tsp) powdered
   turmeric
5 ml (1 tsp) minced
   garlic
20 ml (4 tsp) lemon juice
40 ml (8 tsp) wine vinegar
40 ml (8 tsp) oil
20 ml (4 tsp) whole-grain
   mustard

You can vary the quantities and ingredients according to taste.

Method:

1. Combine ingredients in saucepan and mix to make a smooth paste.
2. Stirring constantly, cook over low heat for 3 – 4 minutes until slightly thickened.
3. Spoon mixture into a warmed glass jar, seal and store in refrigerator.

To store: keep in airtight container in refrigerator for up to one month.

Nutritional data per total quantity: negligible.

Preparation time: 6 minutes. Cooking equipment: saucepan.

Curry Powder

Makes about 90 g
(3 oz, ¾ cup)

2.5 ml (½ tsp) cayenne
   pepper
40 ml (8 tsp) ground
   coriander
20 ml (4 tsp) ground
   cumin
20 ml (4 tsp) coarsely
   ground black pepper
40 ml (8 tsp) ground
   ginger
20 ml (4 tsp) ground
   cinnamon
2.5 ml (½ tsp) ground
   cloves
good pinch of grated
   nutmeg
10 ml (2 tsp) chilli powder
40 ml (8 tsp) powdered
   turmeric

You can vary the ingredients and quantities according to taste. Curry Powder can be stored for a long time, but gradually loses its flavour.

Method:

1. Mix ingredients well.
2. Refrigerate in airtight container.

Nutritional data per total quantity: negligible.

Preparation time: 15 minutes.

QUICK AND EASY MARINADES

Try these marinades with lean beef steaks, lamb cutlets, pork chops or as a marinade for meat to place on skewers; excellent for barbecue or grill. These quantities are for 500 g (1 lb) meat and will serve four.

Red Wine Zap:

Combine 125 ml (4 fl oz, 1/2 cup) dry red wine, 20 ml (4 tsp) tomato paste, 20 ml (4 tsp) Worcestershire sauce, 40 ml (8 tsp) finely chopped parsley, 1 crushed garlic clove, ground black pepper to taste and good pinch finely chopped oregano or basil (optional).

To rev it up – add 60 ml (2 fl oz, 1/4 cup) sweet chilli sauce, 60 ml (2 fl oz, 1/4 cup) Worcestershire sauce, or 1 – 2 crushed garlic cloves. Stir ingredients and use to brush meat as it grills.

Singapore Sizzler:

Combine 20 ml (4 tsp) Worcestershire sauce, 20 ml (4 tsp) soy or teriyaki sauce, 40 ml (8 tsp) lemon juice, good pinch of mustard powder, good pinch of ground coriander and good pinch of chopped fresh ginger. Stir the ingredients and use to brush meat as it grills.

Spicy Lamb:

Particularly good for lamb is a combination of 125 ml (4 fl oz, 1/2 cup) tomato paste, 10 ml (2 tsp) Worcestershire sauce, 10 ml (2 tsp) chopped fresh or 2.5 ml (1/2 tsp) dried rosemary, dash of Tabasco and 4 chopped spring onions (shallots). Stir the ingredients and use to brush meat as it grills.

SWEET SAUCES

Creamy Whipped Topping

Makes about 450 ml (¾ pint, 2 cups)

45 g (1 ½ oz, ½ cup)
  skimmed milk powder
250 ml (8 fl oz, 1 cup)
  iced water
few drops vanilla essence

Mixture will lose its thickness after 2 – 3 hours, just re-whip it.

Method:
1. Combine all ingredients in a bowl.
2. With electric beater, hand beater or whisk, beat mixture until thick and creamy. Chill.

Nutritional data per total quantity: 680 kJ (163 cal), CHO 24 g, Protein 16 g, Fat 1 g.
Preparation time: 10 minutes.

Custard Sauce

Serves 4

30 g (1 oz) custard
  powder
500 ml (17 fl oz)
  skimmed milk
few drops of vanilla
  essence
10 ml (2 tsp) sugar or
  artificial sweetener

You can serve this sauce hot or cold.

Method:

1. Blend custard powder and a small quantity of the milk to make a smooth paste.
2. Place remaining milk in saucepan and bring to the boil.
3. Gradually stir in custard paste. Continue stirring until mixture thickens.
4. Simmer for 1 minute, stirring constantly.
5. Add vanilla and sugar or artificial sweetener.

Nutritional data per serve: 298 kJ (71 cal), CHO 13 g, Protein 5 g, Fat trace.

Preparation time: 15 minutes. Cooking equipment: saucepan.

Orange Custard Sauce

Follow the recipe for Custard Sauce (above) and add 5 ml (1 tsp) finely grated orange rind to milk before heating.

Brandy Sauce

Serves 4

1 quantity Custard
  Sauce (this page)
1 egg, separated
40 ml (8 tsp) brandy

Method:

1. Beat egg yolk and add to Custard Sauce.
2. Whip egg white until peaks form.
3. Fold egg white through custard and add brandy.
4. Serve immediately.

Nutritional data per serve: 462 kJ (110 cal), CHO 13 g, Protein 6 g, Fat 1 g.

Preparation time: 20 minutes. Cooking equipment: saucepan.

Desserts

Apple Layer Cake

Serves 10 – 12

Biscuits:

125 g (4 oz, 1 cup)
  wholemeal self-raising
  flour
125 g (4 oz) low-fat soft
  cheese
1 egg
few drops vanilla essence
10 ml (2 tsp) soft brown
  sugar

Filling:

500 g (1 lb, 2½ cups)
  cold, stewed apple,
  flavoured with lemon
  rind, cinnamon and
  cloves to taste

Topping:

125 g (4 oz) low-fat soft
  cheese
10 ml (2 tsp) sugar
rind of ½ lemon, finely
  grated
125 g (4 oz) ricotta cheese
good pinch of ground
  cinnamon

Decoration:

60 g (2 oz) pecan nuts,
  chopped

Refrigerate this glorious cake for a day before you serve it so that it is easy to cut and the filling has developed its full flavour.

Method:

Biscuits:

1. Sift flour into bowl. Return bran to sifted flour.
2. Soften cheese and beat with a spoon until smooth. Add egg and vanilla and beat again. Add sugar and mix well.
3. Gradually blend flour into cheese mixture until a soft dough is formed.
4. Turn out on to a floured board and knead into a ball.
5. Divide into three. Shape and roll into rounds about 25 cm (10 inches) in diameter, making them as equal as possible.
6. Lift on to very lightly greased baking sheets.
7. Bake in a preheated oven for 12 minutes until cooked through and light brown.
8. Remove and cool on wire racks.

Filling:

9. Add lemon rind, cinnamon and cloves to taste to cold, stewed apple. Mixture should be fairly firm.

Topping:

10. Beat low-fat soft cheese until smooth. Add sugar, lemon rind, ricotta and cinnamon and mix well.

Assembly:

11. Place one biscuit-round on serving plate. Cover with half the apple. Cover with the second round, spread with the remainder of the apple, then place third round on top.
12. Spread topping mixture on top and sides of cake.
13. Sprinkle with pecans, cover with clingfilm (plastic wrap) and refrigerate for at least 24 hours.
14. Cut into wedges to serve.

Nutritional data per serve (if 10 serves): 763 kJ (182 cal), CHO 17 g, Protein 6 g, Fat 10 g.

Preparation time: biscuits 30 minutes, assembly 30 minutes, begin preparation 24 hours before serving. Cooking equipment: 2 baking sheets, wire rack. Oven temperature: 180 °C (350 °F, gas 4).

Fruit Strudel

Apple Strudel
Serves 4

6 sheets filo pastry

40 ml (8 tsp) skimmed
  milk

4 apples, peeled and
  sliced very finely

45 g (½ oz) sultanas

40 ml (8 tsp) chopped
  pecan nuts

5 ml (1 tsp) ground
  cinnamon

good pinch of ground
  cloves

20 ml (4 tsp) soft brown
  sugar

As tasty as traditional strudel but with a fraction of the fat.

Method:

1. Spread out two sheets of pastry on a work surface. Brush lightly with milk.
2. Place another two layers of pastry on top. Again brush with milk.
3. Repeat with remaining two sheets of pastry.
4. Sprinkle remaining ingredients over the pastry.
5. Grease a baking sheet lightly. Carefully roll up the pastry. Place on the baking sheet, loose edge down.
6. Brush the strudel well with milk. Bake in a preheated oven for 25 – 30 minutes.

Serve warm, cut in thick slices. You may serve this with Creamy Whipped Topping (page 163).

Nutritional data per serve: 800 kJ (191 cal), CHO 36 g,
Protein 5 g, Fat 5 g.

Preparation time: 45 minutes. Cooking equipment: baking sheet. Oven temperature: 200 °C (400 °F, gas 6).

Banana Strudel

The basic method is exactly the same as for Apple Strudel (see above); only the filling is different. For this delectable filling combine: four ripe bananas, sliced, 90 g (3 oz) sultanas, 5 ml (1 tsp) ground cinnamon, 15 g (1/2 oz) shredded coconut, 40 ml (8 tsp) unsweetened orange juice, 40 ml (8 tsp) chopped pecan nuts or walnuts, 75 ml (21/2 fl oz) dark rum and 5 ml (1 tsp) soft brown sugar.

Apricot Strudel

The basic method is exactly the same as for Apple Strudel (see above); only the filling is different. Here you combine: 500 g (1 lb) apricots, stoned and sliced, or 410 g (14 oz) canned unsweetened apricot pieces, 90 g (3 oz) sultanas, 40 ml (8 tsp) slivered almonds, 5 ml (1 tsp) ground cinnamon and 20 ml (4 tsp) soft brown sugar.

Ricotta Raisin Flan

Serves 6 – 8

60 g (2 oz) margarine

125 g (4 oz) shredded
  wheatmeal biscuits,
  crushed

500 g (1 lb) ricotta cheese

75 ml (2½ fl oz) apple
  concentrate

170 g (6 oz, 1 cup)
  raisins, chopped

rind of 1 lemon, grated

2.5 ml (½ tsp) ground
  cinnamon

good pinch of grated
  nutmeg

1 egg

125 ml (4 fl oz, ½ cup)
  low-fat milk

garnish: ground
  cinnamon

Method:

1. Melt margarine, then pour over biscuit crumbs and mix well.
2. Spread over base and up sides of pie dish. Press down well to make an even, firm crust.
3. Bake in a preheated oven for 10 minutes. Cool.
4. Mix ricotta, apple concentrate, raisins, lemon rind and spices.
5. Beat egg and combine with milk. Mix it with other ingredients. Blend well.
6. Pour into pie dish. Bake in a preheated oven for about 30 – 45 minutes until set and lightly browned.
7. Sprinkle with a little cinnamon and serve.

To store: cover and refrigerate for up to two days.

Nutritional data per serve: 1562 kJ (373 cal), CHO 43 g, Protein 13 g, Fat 17 g.

Preparation time: 1 hour 50 minutes. Cooking equipment: small saucepan, pie dish. Oven temperature: 180 °C (350 °F, gas 4).

Lemon Delight

Serves 4

3 eggs

100 ml (3 ½ fl oz) fresh
  lemon juice

rind of 1 lemon, freshly
  grated

20 ml (4 tsp) melted
  butter

30 g (1 oz) wholemeal
  plain flour

350 ml (12 fl oz,
  1 ½ cups) low-fat milk

20 ml (4 tsp) sugar or
  equivalent artificial
  sweetener

Method:

1. Separate eggs. Beat egg whites until stiff peaks form.
2. Beat yolks with the remaining ingredients until smooth.
3. Gradually fold the egg whites into mixture.
4. Spoon evenly into four dishes.
5. Place in a larger baking dish. Carefully pour water into the larger baking dish until it reaches two-thirds up the outside of the individual baking dishes.
6. Bake in a preheated oven for 20 minutes or until set and lightly browned.
7. Cool slightly in the water-filled dish to prevent shrinking.

To store: cover and refrigerate for one day only.

Nutritional data per serve: 886 kJ (212 cal), CHO 12 g, Protein 9 g, Fat 14 g.

Preparation time: 1 hour. Cooking equipment: individual baking dishes, large baking dish for water bath. Oven temperature: 160 °C (325 °F, gas 3).

Spiced Oranges

Serves 4

250 ml (8 fl oz, 1 cup)
  red wine, such as claret
  or burgundy
125 ml (4 fl oz, ½ cup)
  unsweetened orange
  juice
good pinch of ground
  cinnamon or
  1 cinnamon stick
3 oranges
artificial sweetener to
  taste

The ideal dessert after a long, hot summer's day.

Method:

1. Place wine, orange juice and cinnamon in a saucepan and bring to the boil.
2. Boil vigorously for 2 minutes, then remove from heat, or microwave on High for 2 – 3 minutes.
3. Peel and thinly slice oranges, removing all pith and seeds, and arrange in a glass serving bowl.
4. Pour wine mixture over oranges, discarding cinnamon stick if using.
5. Chill well and sweeten before serving.

To store: cover and refrigerate for up to four days.

Nutritional data per serve: 219 kJ (52 cal), CHO 11 g, Protein 1 g, Fat trace.
Preparation time: 15 minutes. Cooking equipment: saucepan.

Creamy Rice

Serves 4

200 g (7 oz, 1 cup) brown
  rice
350 ml (12 fl oz,
  1 ½ cups) water
600 ml (1 pint, 2 ½ cups)
  skimmed or low-fat
  milk
90 g (3 oz, ½ cup)
  sultanas
2.5 ml (½ tsp) grated
  nutmeg
few drops of vanilla
  essence
artificial sweetener
  equivalent to 20 ml
  (4 tsp) sugar

Method:

1. Wash rice and place in saucepan, cover with the water, and simmer over very low heat until water is absorbed.
2. Add 250 ml (8 fl oz, 1 cup) milk. Simmer again until absorbed.
3. Add the remaining milk and cook again until the milk is absorbed.
4. Stir in sultanas, nutmeg, vanilla and sweetener to taste.
5. Serve warm with sliced, stewed or fresh fruit.

To store: cover and refrigerate for up to three days.

Nutritional data per serve: 1185 kJ (283 cal), CHO 58 g, Protein 10 g, Fat 1 g.

Preparation time: 1½ hours. Cooking equipment: saucepan.

Fruit Crumble

Serves 4

3 large cooking apples,
  peeled, cored and sliced
40 ml (8 tsp) water
2.5 ml (½ tsp) ground
  cinnamon, or 3 whole
  cloves
Topping:
170 g (6 oz, 1 ⅓ cups)
  Meg's Muesli (page 58)
  or 45 g (1 ½ oz, ½ cup)
  rolled oats
40 ml (8 tsp) desiccated
  coconut
40 ml (8 tsp) mixed dried
  fruit
10 ml (2 tsp) chopped
  nuts
15 g (½ oz, ¼ cup)
  wheatflakes
15 g (½ oz, ¼ cup)
  All Bran

You can replace the apples in this recipe with peaches, apricots or plums or with two apples and 60 g (2 oz, 1/2 cup) cooked rhubarb. If you have a favourite combination, you can use it in this recipe too.

Method:
1. Place apple in a saucepan, add water and cinnamon or cloves.
2. Gently simmer for about 10 minutes until apple is tender, or microwave, covered, on High for 6 minutes.
3. Lightly grease a small casserole and spoon in apple, removing cloves if using.
4. Mix topping ingredients and sprinkle thickly over apple.
5. Bake in a preheated oven for 30 minutes or until topping becomes golden.
6. Serve hot or cold.

To store: cover and refrigerate for up to four days.

Nutritional data per serve: 1025 kJ (245 cal), CHO 38 g, Protein 7 g, Fat 7 g.

Preparation time: 1 hour. Cooking equipment: saucepan, small casserole. Oven temperature: 180 °C (350 °F, gas 4).

Summer Pudding

Serves 4

14 slices of wholemeal
  bread
1 kg (2 lb, 6 cups) mixed
  fresh berries (straw-
  berries, raspberries,
  blueberries,
  loganberries)
20 ml (4 tsp) caster sugar
garnish: extra berries

Method:
1. Cut crusts off bread and discard them.
2. Cut four round bases and tops out of crustless bread. Set tops aside. Place a base in each individual soufflé dish. Use the remaining bread to line the sides of the dishes. Do this carefully, making sure that there are no gaps.
3. Wash and hull berries. Chop strawberries.
4. Place berries and sugar in saucepan and heat gently until liquid runs from berries.
5. Fill soufflé dishes, packing fruit down firmly, and pour juice over.

6. Cover each with one of the reserved tops.
7. Place a weight on top and refrigerate overnight.
8. Remove and discard the tops.
9. Turn on to serving dishes. Garnish with extra berries.

Nutritional data per serve: 876 kJ (209 cal), CHO 42 g, Protein 7 g, Fat 1 g.

Preparation time: 20 minutes, plus overnight standing time. Cooking equipment: 4 individual soufflé dishes, saucepan.

Pumpkin Pie

Serves 6

Pastry:
60 g (2 oz) margarine
125 g (4 oz, 1 cup)
  wholemeal flour
1 egg yolk
juice of ½ lemon, plus
  cold water to make up
  75 ml (2½ fl oz,
  ⅓ cup)
Filling:
500 g (1 lb, 2 cups) firm
  pumpkin purée
60 g (2 oz, ¼ cup) ricotta
  cheese
60 ml (2 fl oz, ¼ cup) low-
  fat plain yoghurt
125 ml (4 fl oz, ½ cup)
  skimmed or low-fat
  milk
2 eggs, separated
good pinch of grated
  nutmeg
good pinch of mixed
  spice
2.5 ml (½ tsp) ground
  cinnamon
juice and grated rind of
  1 lemon
artificial sweetener to
  taste
garnish: ground
  cinnamon

This is simply delicious!

Method:

Pastry:
1. Rub margarine into flour until mixture resembles fine breadcrumbs.
2. Mix egg yolk with lemon juice and water.
3. Mix liquid into flour with a knife, to make a soft dough.
4. Turn out on to floured board. Knead lightly and leave for 15 minutes.
5. Roll out on floured board, then cover base and sides of pie dish with pastry. Add a second strip around the top edge and pinch as a decorative edge. Prick pastry and bake in a preheated oven for about 1 hour until lightly browned. Remove and cool.

Filling:
6. Combine in a bowl pumpkin, ricotta, yoghurt, milk and egg yolks. Beat well.
7. Add spices, lemon juice and rind, and sweetener. Check taste and adjust if necessary.
8. Beat egg whites until soft peaks form; fold into pumpkin mixture.
9. Pour into pastry shell and bake in a preheated oven until set (about 1 hour).
10. Sprinkle with a little cinnamon to serve.

To vary: fold 30 g (1 oz, 1/4 cup) chopped pecan nuts into filling.

To store: cover and refrigerate for up to two days.

Nutritional data per serve: 851 kJ (203 cal), CHO 20 g, Protein 9 g, Fat 10 g.

Preparation time: 2 hours. Cooking equipment: pie dish.
Oven temperature: 180 °C (350 °F, gas 4).

Mixed Berry Salad with Lemon Cream

Serves 4

Salad:

250 g (8 oz) strawberries

250 g (8 oz) blackberries

250 g (8 oz) blueberries

60 ml (2 fl oz, ¼ cup)
    unsweetened apple
    juice

Lemon cream:

250 g (8 oz) ricotta cheese

100 g (3½ oz) low-fat
    plain yoghurt

rind of 1 lemon, grated

10 ml (2 tsp) soft brown
    sugar

When berries are in season, celebrate with this salad dressed with smooth lemon cream.

Method:

1. Wash and hull berries, slice strawberries if large.
2. Place in bowl and pour apple juice over.
3. Chill in refrigerator.

Lemon cream:

4. Mix ricotta, yoghurt, lemon rind and sugar.
5. Chill
6. Spoon lemon cream over fruit and serve

To vary: replace blackberries with loganberries

Nutritional data per serve: 419 kJ (100 cal), CHO 20 g, Protein 4 g, Fat 1 g.

Preparation time: 30 minutes.

Hot Jamaican Pineapple

Serves 4

½ medium pineapple, cut
    lengthwise with top
    intact

3 bananas, peeled and
    chopped

20 ml (4 tsp) dark rum

10 ml (2 tsp) soft brown
    sugar

15 g (½ oz, ¼ cup)
    desiccated coconut

Method:

1. Cut pineapple out of skin, being careful not to pierce skin. Scoop out any remaining pulp and juice and retain.
2. Chop pineapple into chunks, discarding core. Add to pulp and juice in bowl. Add bananas. Add rum and brown sugar.
3. Spoon fruit and juices into shell and sprinkle with coconut.
4. Place in baking dish, and bake in a preheated oven for 30 – 45 minutes until fruit is heated through and coconut is toasted.
5. Spoon into serving dishes.

Nutritional data per serve: 542 kJ (130 cal), CHO 25 g, Protein 2 g, Fat 2 g.

Preparation time: 1 hour. Cooking equipment: baking dish. Oven temperature 180 °C (350 °F, gas 4).

Ginger Pears

Serves 4

4 medium pears, peeled
   and quartered
300 ml (½ pint) low-
   calorie (low-joule) dry
   ginger ale
2.5 ml (½ tsp) minced
   fresh ginger
60 ml (2 fl oz, ¼ cup)
   orange juice
   concentrate
3 – 4 drops yellow food
   colouring (optional)
6 whole cloves
garnish: ground
   cinnamon

Method:

1. Place pears in saucepan. Add dry ginger ale, lemon juice, ginger, orange juice concentrate, food colouring and cloves.
2. Cover and simmer until pears are tender, turning and basting the pears so they cook and colour evenly. Alternatively, microwave, covered, on High for 4 – 6 minutes until tender.
3. Lift pears on to serving dish.
4. Simmer juice until slightly reduced.
5. Pour over pears. Sprinkle with cinnamon.
6. Serve hot or chilled.

To store: cover and refrigerate for up to four days.

Nutritional data per serve: 382 kJ (91 cal), CHO 22 g, Protein 1 g, Fat 0 g.

Preparation time: 1 hour. Cooking equipment: saucepan.

Fruity Baked Rice Pudding

Serves 4

900 ml (1½ pints,
   3½ cups) skimmed milk
90 g (3 oz) brown or
   white rice
20 ml (4 tsp) sugar
60 g (2 oz) sultanas or
   raisins
60 g (2 oz) dried peaches
   or apricots, chopped
garnish: grated nutmeg
   or ground cinnamon

Method:

1. Combine milk, rice and sugar.
2. Place mixture in baking dish.
3. Cover and bake in a preheated oven for 45 minutes.
4. Remove from oven, add dried fruit and stir.
5. Leave uncovered and return to oven. Cook for another 45 – 60 minutes until rice is cooked. A skin will form on top of the rice.
6. Serve hot or cold, garnished with grated nutmeg or cinnamon.

To store: cover and refrigerate for up to three days.

Nutritional data per serve: 1191 kJ (284 cal), CHO 60 g, Protein 11 g, Fat trace.

Preparation time: 2 hours. Cooking equipment: baking dish with lid. Oven temperature: 180 °C (350 °F, gas 4).

Old-Fashioned Dumplings

Serves 4

175 ml (6 fl oz, ¾ cup)
  skimmed or low-fat milk
good pinch of grated
  nutmeg
90 g (3 oz, ½ cup)
  semolina
1 egg
few drops of vanilla
  essence
20 ml (4 tsp) mixed peel
20 ml (4 tsp) currants
20 ml (4 tsp) sultanas
plain flour
250 ml (8 fl oz, 1 cup)
  Orange Custard
  Sauce (page 164) or
  apple purée

Method:

1. Place milk and nutmeg in small saucepan and bring to the boil.
2. Remove from heat and quickly stir in semolina.
3. Return to heat and stir for 1 minute.
4. Add egg, vanilla, peel, currants and sultanas and mix well.
5. Turn on to a lightly floured board and knead gently till smooth.
6. Break off small, even-sized pieces and roll into balls the size of large marbles. Toss each ball in flour.
7. Half-fill a large saucepan with water and bring to the boil.
8. Drop dumplings into boiling water and cook for about 5 minutes. (Note: the dumplings will rise to the top of the water as they cook.)
9. Drain and serve immediately with Orange Custard Sauce (page 164) or apple purée.

Nutritional data per serve: 584 kJ (140 cal), CHO 24 g, Protein 7 g, Fat 2 g.

Preparation time: 20 minutes plus preparation time for sauce.
Cooking equipment: small saucepan, large saucepan.

Baked Apples with Orange and Strawberry Sauce

Serves 4

4 Granny Smith apples
2.5 ml (½ tsp) ground
  cinnamon
250 ml (8 fl oz, 1 cup)
  orange juice
250 g (8 oz) strawberries
liquid artificial
  sweetener to taste
40 ml (8 tsp) slivered
  almonds or chopped
  pecans
orange slices

Method:

1. Peel and core apples. When peeling leave some peel on to create a horizontal striped effect.
2. Place in a small baking dish. Sprinkle cinnamon over, then orange juice.
3. Bake apples in a preheated oven for 30 – 35 minutes, or microwave on High for 6 – 8 minutes, until tender but still retaining their shape. Baste occasionally to prevent drying out.
4. While apples are cooking, wash and hull strawberries and purée them. Add sweetener to purée.
5. When apples are cooked, lift gently on to individual serving dishes.

6. Reduce cooking liquid by boiling if necessary and pour into strawberry purée. Mix and pour over apples.
7. Decorate with slivered or chopped nuts and orange slices.
8. Serve warm or chilled.

To store: cover and refrigerate for up to two days.

Nutritional data per serve: 387 kJ (92 cal), CHO 18 g, Protein 2 g, Fat 1 g.

Preparation time: 1 hour. Cooking equipment: food processor, baking dish, small saucepan. Oven temperature: 180 °C (350 °F, gas 4).

Fruit Compote

Serves 4

1 small apple, peeled, cored and cut into 8 wedges

90 g (3 oz, 1 cup) canned unsweetened peaches in natural juice

1 small pear, peeled, cored and cut into 8 wedges

12 whole cherries

4 yellow plums, cut into half and stoned

2 whole cloves

pinch of ground cinnamon

This is usually a chilled dessert but you can serve it hot. Vary the fruit according to season and your preference; for instance, if fresh plums are not available, use canned, unsweetened apricot halves or peach slices which you add after the other fruit has been cooked.

Method:
1. Place ingredients in saucepan, with apple at the bottom and peaches at the top.
2. Bring to the boil and simmer gently for 10 minutes or until all fruit is tender.
3. Cool and place in refrigerator for at least 2 hours before serving in glass dishes.

To store: cover and refrigerate for up to three days.

Microwave: place fruit in microwave dish, cover and cook on Medium for 5 minutes.

Nutritional data per serve: 283 kJ (68 cal), CHO 16 g, Protein 1 g, Fat 0 g.

Preparation time: 2 hours 20 minutes including cooling time. Cooking equipment: medium saucepan.

Baked Custard

Serves 4

2 eggs

liquid artificial
  sweetener to taste

325 ml (11 fl oz, 1⅓ cups)
  skimmed milk

few drops of vanilla
  essence

sprinkling of grated
  nutmeg

This family favourite can be served hot or cold.

Method:

1. In bowl, lightly beat the eggs.
2. Gradually add the milk to the egg mixture, stirring constantly. Stir in the vanilla essence and sweetener. Check flavour.
3. Pour mixture into a pie or soufflé dish or dishes. Sprinkle with nutmeg.
4. Stand the baking dish(es) in a large baking dish. Carefully pour enough water into the large baking dish to reach two-thirds up the outside of the pie or soufflé dish(es).
5. Bake in a preheated oven for 35 minutes if you are using individual dishes, 45 minutes if you are using one big dish. The custard should be lightly browned and set in the centre.

Nutritional data per serve: 266 kJ (63 cal), CHO 4 g, Protein 6 g, Fat 3 g.

Preparation time: 1 hour 10 minutes. Cooking equipment: deep pie or soufflé dish or 4 individual ovenproof dishes, large baking dish for water bath. Oven temperature: 150 °C (300 °F, gas 2).

Dessert Ideas for Pancakes and Crêpes

Crêpes Suzette

4 oranges, peeled and cut
  into segments, pith
  removed

juice of 1 orange

60 ml (2 fl oz, ¼ cup)
  brandy

12 Crêpes (page 82)
  warmed

garnish: grated orange
  rind

Method:

1. Poach orange segments gently in orange juice until heated through.
2. Drain off juice and set aside.
3. Add brandy to fruit in frying pan, heat and ignite with a match or a lighter. Stir fruit gently and allow brandy to burn out.
5. Pour juice back into pan and reheat.
6. Place Crêpes one by one in pan, filling each with fruit and folding each into four to make a triangle. This allows Crêpes to absorb the juice.
7. Serve topped with a sprinkling of orange rind.

Flambéed Pancakes
or Crêpes

a mixture of fruits, for
instance:

250 g (8 oz) strawberries,
washed and hulled

2 bananas, sliced

8 apricots, stoned and
quartered

juice of 1 orange

2.5 ml (½ tsp) ground
cinnamon

75 ml (2½ fl oz) brandy

8 Pancakes (page 83) or
12 Crêpes (page 82),
warmed

Method:

1. In a frying pan, combine fruit and juice and simmer gently for about 5 minutes until fruit heats through and softens.
2. Drain off juice and set aside.
3. Add brandy to pan, heat and ignite with a match or lighter. Stir fruit gently and allow brandy to burn out.
4. Pour juice back into pan and reheat.
5. Divide fruit evenly between Pancakes or Crêpes and roll up or, if using Crêpes, fold into four to make triangles.

Berry and Cheese
Pancakes

250 g (8 oz, 2 cups)
mixed berries, washed
and hulled

5 ml (1 tsp) water

8 Pancakes (page 83),
warmed

125 g (4 oz) soft cheese

Method:

1. Poach berries in water for about 3 minutes until soft.
2. Divide fruit evenly between Pancakes and top each with about 40 ml (8 tsp) soft cheese.
3. Roll up and serve hot.

Apple and Sultana
Pancakes

4 apples, peeled, cored
and sliced

2 whole cloves

45 g (1½ oz) sultanas

8 Pancakes (page 83),
warmed

Method:

1. Poach apples gently in a little water with cloves and sultanas for about 5 minutes until soft. Alternatively, microwave, covered, on High for 5 – 8 minutes.
2. Remove cloves and divide apple mixture evenly between Pancakes.
3. Roll up and serve hot.

Golden Fruit Flummery

Serves 12

1 pkt low-calorie (low-
joule) jelly crystals,
orange or orange and
mango flavours
375 ml (12 fl oz, 1½ cups)
boiling water
125 ml (4 fl oz, ½ cup)
canned evaporated
skimmed milk, chilled
410 g (14 oz) canned
unsweetened peach
pieces, puréed
1 large mango, puréed
garnish: Creamy
Whipped Topping
(page 163) and sprig
of mint

To prevent the evaporated milk separating from the rest of the flummery, you need to have the jelly and milk mixtures at about the same temperature before you combine them. Vary this recipe by puréeing 410 g (14 oz) canned unsweetened apricot pieces instead of peaches and mango.

Method:
1. Dissolve jelly crystals in boiling water, cool, place in refrigerator until just beginning to set.
2. Whip jelly and, as it becomes fluffy, slowly add evaporated skimmed milk, whipping continually until the mixture thickens.
3. Gently mix in puréed fruit and pour into glass dishes.
4. Chill well before serving, garnished with a spoonful of Creamy Whipped Topping and a sprig of mint on each.

To store: cover and refrigerate for up to three days.

Nutritional data per serve: 131 kJ (31 cal), CHO 6 g, Protein 2 g, Fat trace.

Preparation time: 2 hours including time taken to chill jelly. Cooking equipment: electric beater.

Baked Yoghurt Slice

Serves 8

Crust:
12 wheatmeal biscuits or
125 g (4 oz, 1 cup)
Meg's Muesli (page 58)
45 ml (9 tsp)
unsweetened apple
juice
Filling:
250 ml (8 fl oz, 1 cup)
low-fat fruit yoghurt

Method:
1. Grind the biscuits or muesli in food processor or blender, or crush well with rolling pin.
2. Add apple juice to crumbs to make a spreadable mixture.
3. Line flan tin with foil.
4. Press crumb mixture into lined flan tin.
5. Blend yoghurt, ricotta cheese, lemon juice and rind and apple juice in food processor or blender.
6. Beat egg whites until stiff.
7. Fold through the blended cheese mixture with the egg whites and sultanas.

300 g (10 oz, 1¼ cups)
  ricotta cheese
juice of 1 lemon
grated rind of 1 lemon
40 ml (8 tsp)
  unsweetened apple
  juice
2 egg whites
90 g (3 oz, ½ cup)
  sultanas

8. Pour into biscuit base.
9. Bake in a preheated oven for about 30 minutes until firm.
10. Cool and cut into slices.

To vary: use different flavoured yoghurt.

To store: cover with clingfilm (plastic wrap) and refrigerate for up to two days.

Nutritional data per serve: 781 kJ (187 cal), CHO 25 g, Protein 8 g, Fat 6 g.

Preparation time: 1 hour. Cooking equipment: food processor, flan tin. Oven temperature: 180 °C (350 °F, gas 4).

Mocha Mousse

Serves 4

2 eggs, separated
375 ml (12 fl oz) full-
  cream evaporated milk
20 ml (4 tsp) cocoa
  powder
2.5 ml (½ tsp) instant
  coffee granules
15 ml (3 tsp) powdered
  gelatine
60 ml (2 fl oz, ¼ cup)
  water
artificial sweetener
  equivalent to 30 ml
  (6 tsp) sugar
garnish: chopped dates
  or fresh strawberries

This is a scrumptious dessert! Prepare it the day before you want to serve it because it needs time to set.

Method:
1. Beat egg yolks and combine them in a saucepan with milk, cocoa and coffee. Mix until smooth.
2. Stirring constantly, warm the mixture over medium heat, being careful not to boil it. Remove from heat and cool.
3. Sprinkle gelatine over water and dissolve over hot water, or microwave on Medium for 10 seconds. Cool slightly.
4. Stir into chocolate mixture. Add sweetener.
5. Beat egg whites until soft peaks form. Fold into chocolate mixture.
6. Pour into serving dishes. Cover and refrigerate overnight.
7. Serve chilled, garnished with chopped dates or strawberries.

Nutritional data per serve: 169 kJ (40 cal), CHO 2 g, Protein 3 g, Fat 2 g.

Preparation time: 45 minutes plus setting time. Cooking equipment: saucepan.

Bread and Butter Pudding

Serves 4

4 eggs

600 ml (1 pint, 2 ½ cups)
skimmed or low-fat
milk

few drops of vanilla
essence

3 slices of wholemeal
bread

10 ml (2 tsp) margarine

45 g (1 ½ oz) sultanas

5 ml (1 tsp) grated
nutmeg

Method:

1. Place eggs in bowl and beat.
2. Add milk and vanilla essence.
3. Spread bread with margarine and cut each slice into four squares.
4. Place three squares in each individual baking dish.
5. Pour an equal amount of the mixture into each dish.
6. Sprinkle sultanas and nutmeg evenly into the four dishes.
7. Place the four individual dishes in a larger baking dish and carefully pour water into the larger baking dish to reach two-thirds up the outside of the individual baking dishes.
8. Bake in a preheated oven for 30 – 45 minutes until set, or arrange the puddings in a wide circle in the microwave to ensure even cooking.

Microwave: on Medium for 8 – 10 minutes.

Nutritional data per serve: 837 kJ (200 cal), CHO 19 g, Protein 13 g, Fat 8 g.

Preparation time: 1 hour. Cooking equipment: individual baking dishes, large baking dish for water bath. Oven temperature: 180 °C (350 °F, gas 4).

Queen's Pudding

Serves 4

4 eggs

600 ml (1 pint, 2 ½ cups)
skimmed or low-fat
milk

few drops of vanilla
essence

3 slices of wholemeal
bread, crumbed

75 ml (2½ fl oz)
strawberry or
raspberry purée

20 ml (4 tsp) caster sugar

If you do not have any strawberry or raspberry purée you can use low-calorie (low-kilojoule) jam as a substitute.

Method:

1. Separate two of the eggs and set egg whites aside.
2. Combine egg yolks with the other two whole eggs and beat.
3. Add milk and vanilla.
4. Distribute breadcrumbs evenly between four individual baking dishes.
5. Pour equal amounts of custard mixture into each dish.
6. Put individual dishes in a larger baking dish and carefully pour in water until it reaches two-thirds up the outside of the individual baking dishes. Bake in a preheated oven for 30 – 45 minutes.

7. When cooked, carefully spread top of custard with fruit purée.
8. Beat the remaining two egg whites until they are stiff and fold in caster sugar and pile over purée.
9. Bake for about 5 minutes until meringue is lightly browned.

To store: cover and refrigerate for up to two days.

Nutritional data per serve: 793 kJ (189 cal), CHO 21 g, Protein 13 g, Fat 6 g.

Preparation time: $1^{1}/2$ hours. Cooking equipment: individual baking dishes, large baking dish for water bath. Oven temperature: 180 °C (350 °F, gas 4).

Christmas Pudding

Serves 6

60 g (2 oz) sultanas
30 g (1 oz) currants
45 g (1½ oz) raisins
grated rind of 1 orange
60 g (2 oz, ½ cup) grated carrot, apple or cooked pumpkin (or a mixture of 2)
60 ml (2 fl oz, ¼ cup) brandy
60 g (2 oz, ½ cup) wholemeal flour
5 ml (1 tsp) ground cinnamon
5 ml (1 tsp) mixed spice
2.5 ml (½ tsp) grated nutmeg
30 g (1 oz) margarine
1½ slices of wholemeal bread, crumbed
1 egg, lightly beaten
75 ml (2½ fl oz, ⅓ cup) skimmed or low-fat milk
few drops of vanilla essence
20 ml (4 tsp) brown sugar or artificial sweetener
2.5 ml (½ tsp) bicarbonate of soda
20 ml (4 tsp) hot water

This is better if made a week before you want to serve it, so that the flavours have time to mature.

Method:
1. Soak dried fruit, orange rind and carrot, apple or pumpkin in brandy overnight.
2. Mix flour and spices.
3. Rub margarine into flour mixture and add breadcrumbs.
4. Add egg, milk, fruit mixture, vanilla essence and sugar or sweetener.
5. Mix bicarbonate of soda and hot water, add to other ingredients and mix well.
6. Pour into a greased bowl, cover securely and steam for 1½ – 2 hours.
7. Turn out and serve with Brandy Sauce (page 164).

To store: in refrigerator. Reheat by steaming or boiling for 30 – 45 minutes until heated through, or microwave, covered on High for 5 – 7 minutes. Do not store the pudding again after you have reheated it.

Nutritional data per serve: 1246 kJ (298 cal), CHO 46 g, Protein 10 g, Fat 6 g.

Preparation time: 2½ hours plus overnight soaking. Cooking equipment: pudding basin, steamer or large saucepan.

Melon Sorbet with Blackcurrant or Raspberry Sauce

Serves 4

Sorbet:

½ cantaloup (rock melon)

juice of 1 lemon

artificial sweetener
  equivalent to 10 ml
  (2 tsp) sugar

1 egg white, beaten until
  stiff

Sauce:

150 g (5 oz, 1 cup)
  blackcurrants or 200 g
  (7 oz, 1½ cups)
  raspberries, rinsed and
  hulled

175 – 250 ml (6 – 8 fl oz,
  ¾ – 1 cup) water

good pinch of ground
  cinnamon

10 ml (2 tsp) cornflour
  (cornstarch)

20 ml (4 tsp) water

artificial sweetener
  equivalent to
  20 – 40 ml (2 – 4 tsp)
  sugar

The key to a smooth sorbet is in the beating during the freezing process, which ensures that the ice crystals which form are small and even.

Method:

Sorbet:

1. Seed and peel cantaloup (rock melon).
2. Cut into pieces and blend in food processor or blender until smooth.
3. Add lemon juice and sweetener and blend again.
4. Pour into container, cover and freeze for 2 – 3 hours until just set.
5. Blend again in food processor or blender, or use an electric beater. The mixture should become creamy.
6. Fold in egg white.
7. Refreeze.
8. Before serving, remove sorbet from freezer and allow to soften a little.
9. Serve with sauce poured over.

Sauce:

10. Place berries, water and cinnamon in saucepan.
11. Heat gently until fruit has softened and lost its shape. Remove from heat.
12. Make a smooth paste of cornflour (cornstarch) and water and add to fruit, stirring well.
13. Reheat until mixture has thickened.
14. Cool and add sweetener to taste.
15. Refrigerate until ready to serve.

Nutritional data per serve: 144 kJ (34 cal), CHO 7 g, Protein 2 g, Fat 0 g.

Preparation time: 1 hour. Cooking equipment: food processor, blender or electric beater, saucepan.

Crunchy Peach Ice-Cream

Serves 6 – 8

410 g (14 oz) canned
    peach pie filling
juice of ½ lemon
2.5 ml (½ tsp) ground
    cinnamon
45 g (1½ oz) ricotta cheese
100 g (3½ oz) low-fat
    plain yoghurt
artificial sweetener to
    taste or 40 ml (8 tsp)
    apple concentrate
10 ml (2 tsp) liqueur
    (optional)
40 ml (8 tsp) shredded
    coconut
40 ml (8 tsp) chopped
    blanched almonds,
    toasted
15 g (½ oz) crunchy cereal
    (muesli, rice bubbles,
    etc.)
1 egg white

The more carefully you beat the mixture during the freezing process, the smoother and creamier your ice-cream will be. Home-made ice-cream is better used fresh as ice-cream tends to go hard if refrozen.

Method:

1. Blend fruit in food processor or blender until smooth and creamy.
2. Add other ingredients, blend well. Add liqueur if desired.
3. Spoon into container. Cover and freeze for 2 – 3 hours until almost set.
4. Remove and thaw slightly. Break up the ice crystals by returning to food processor or blender; blend until creamy, then spoon back into bowl and add coconut, nuts and cereal.
5. Beat egg white until soft peaks form.
6. Fold into ice-cream, cover and refreeze until firm.
7. Remove and allow to thaw a little before serving, as this ice-cream is much more delicious if a little soft.

Nutritional data per serve: 348 kJ (83 cal), CHO 7 g, Protein 4 g, Fat 4 g.

Preparation time: 1 hour over 1 – 2 days. Cooking equipment: food processor or blender, mixing bowl with lid suitable for freezing.

Lemon and Cinnamon Cheesecake

Serves 8

Biscuit base:

125 g (4 oz, 1 cup)
  shredded wheatmeal
  biscuit crumbs

60 g (2 oz) almonds,
  crushed

15 g (½ oz) margarine,
  melted

10 ml (2 tsp) water

10 ml (2 tsp) ground
  cinnamon

Filling:

300 ml (½ pint, 1¼ cups)
  buttermilk

250 g (8 oz) ricotta cheese

juice of 2 lemons

grated rind of 1 lemon

few drops of vanilla
  essence

20 ml (4 tsp) sugar or
  equivalent artificial
  sweetener

20 ml (4 tsp) powdered
  gelatine

40 ml (8 tsp) water

garnish: kiwi fruit,
  strawberries (optional)
  and 10 ml (2 tsp)
  ground cinnamon

You must make this cheesecake the day before you want to serve it to allow the filling to set.

Method:

Biscuit base:

1. Combine all ingredients for biscuit base.
2. Press mixture into a lined pie dish and refrigerate for 30 minutes.

Filling:

3. Mix buttermilk with ricotta cheese, lemon juice, lemon rind, vanilla essence and sugar or artificial sweetener. Beat until smooth and fluffy.
4. Dissolve gelatine in hot water. Cool slightly and fold into buttermilk mixture; blend well.
5. Pour into pie base and refrigerate until set.
6. Next day, decorate with sliced kiwi fruit and a sprinkle of cinnamon.

To vary: replace lemons and lemon rind with the juice and rind of 1 orange.

To store: cover and refrigerate for up to three days.

Nutritional data per serve: 800 kJ (191 cal), CHO 14 g, Protein 7 g, Fat 12 g.

Preparation time: 1 hour including chilling time for the base.
Cooking equipment: pie dish with removeable base, electric beater.

Foreground left: Summer Pudding, at right Lemon and Cinnamon Cheesecake, at centre left Apple Strudel, and Pumpkin Pie at top.

Baking

Herby Corn Muffins

Makes 12

125 g (4 oz, 1 cup)
  plain flour
125 g (4 oz, 1 cup)
  cornmeal
2.5 ml (½ tsp) salt
10 ml (2 tsp) baking
  powder
15 g (½ oz) margarine,
  melted
250 ml (8 fl oz, 1 cup)
  low-fat milk
1 egg, beaten
good pinch of black
  pepper
2.5 ml (½ tsp) dried
  mixed herbs
40 ml (8 tsp) grated low-
  fat hard cheese

These savoury muffins are a great accompaniment to pumpkin or corn chowder. Eat them fresh because they won't keep.

Method:

1. Sift flours, salt and baking powder into a bowl.
2. Mix margarine, milk and egg and add to dry ingredients. Beat until smooth.
3. Fold in seasonings and cheese and spoon mixture into lightly greased muffin tins.
4. Bake in a preheated oven for 15 – 20 minutes until golden brown. Turn out to cool on a wire rack.

Nutritional data per muffin: 471 kJ (112 cal), CHO 17 g, Protein 4 g, Fat 3 g.

Preparation time: 30 minutes. Cooking equipment: muffin tins. Oven temperature 220 °C (425 °F, gas 7).

Front left: Apricot Cooler, in the glass (centre) Kiwi Cooler, top right Cherries and Leben, top left Sangria.

Wholemeal Pastry

*125 g (4 oz, 1 cup)
wholemeal flour
125 g (4 oz, 1 cup) plain
   flour
125 g (4 oz, ½ cup)
   margarine
juice of ½ lemon
125 – 175 ml (4 – 6 fl oz,
   ½ – ¾ cup) iced water*

You can use 250 g (8 oz, 2 cups) wholemeal flour if you like, but the pastry will be heavier than the version we suggest here. A food processor is a great help; it turns pastry-making into a quick and easy process, but be careful not to over-process the pastry or it will become heavy.

Method:

1. Combine the flours in a large bowl.
2. Rub the margarine into the flour until the mixture resembles breadcrumbs.
3. Combine juice and water and add it to the dry ingredients, a little at a time, working it in after each addition, until you have a soft dough.
4. Turn dough on to a lightly-floured surface and knead lightly. Cover and allow to rest before using.
5. Use dough as required.

Note: most pastries need to be baked in a preheated hot oven – 200 °C (400 °F, gas 6) – for 15 minutes, or until lightly browned.

To store: wrap in clingfilm (plastic wrap) and refrigerate for up to two days.

Nutritional data per quantity: 7831 kJ (1871 cal), CHO 193 g, Protein 36 g, Fat 104 g.

Preparation time: 15 minutes. Oven temperature: 200 °C (400 °F, gas 6).

Pikelets

Makes 12 – 16

*90 g (3 oz, ¾ cup) self-
   raising flour
90 g (3 oz, ¾ cup)
   wholemeal self-raising
   flour
1 egg
175 ml (6 fl oz, ¾ cup)
   skimmed or low-fat
   milk
a little oil for frying*

We have given special recipes for conserves and spreads in this book; they are perfect served with these pikelets.

Method:

1. Place flour in basin and make a well in the centre.
2. Beat egg and mix with milk in a small bowl.
3. Pour the egg and milk mixture into the centre of the flour and gradually beat in the flour using a wooden spoon.
4. Beat mixture well.
5. Heat frying pan and lightly oil.
6. Drop spoonfuls of mixture into pan allowing room for each pikelet to spread.

7. When mixture begins to bubble, turn over with a knife or egg slice.
8. Allow pikelets to cook until light brown on each side, then lift on to a clean cloth. Leave covered with cloth to keep them soft.
9. Serve with Fresh Strawberry Conserve (page 60), Dried Apricot Conserve (page 61) or Date and Fig Spread (page 60).

Nutritional data per pikelet (if 12 made): 341 kJ (81 cal), CHO 13 g, Protein 3 g, Fat 2 g.

Preparation time: 30 minutes. Cooking equipment: large frying pan.

Quick Wholemeal Bread

**Makes 2 loaves,
18 slices each**

*1 kg (2 lbs, 4 cups)
wholemeal flour*
*10 ml (2 tsp) bicarbonate
of soda*
*500 ml (17 fl oz) full-
cream plain yoghurt*
*20 ml (4 tsp) clear honey
(optional)*
*topping: sesame seeds
(optional)*

This quick and easy loaf contains no yeast, so there is no kneading and rising time required. You can vary the recipe by adding 60 g (2 oz, 1/2 cup) roughly chopped pecan nuts or walnuts. Alternatively, try adding 60 g (2 oz, 1/2 cup) sunflower seeds or 90 g (3 oz, 1/2 cup) raisins. You may prefer the flavour of the loaf with the addition of a little salt at Step 3, but try it without first.

Method:
1. Lightly grease the loaf tin.
2. Measure the flour, unsifted, into a large bowl.
3. Add all remaining ingredients, except the sesame seeds. Use a wooden spoon to mix lightly but thoroughly until mixture is fluffy.
4. Spoon mixture into the greased loaf tin. Sprinkle with sesame seeds.
5. Bake in a preheated oven for 50 – 60 minutes, or until loaf sounds hollow when tapped.

To store: keep in an airtight container for up to two days.

Nutritional data per slice: 280 kJ (67 cal), CHO 11 g, Protein 3 g, Fat 1 g.

Preparation time: about 1 hour. Cooking equipment: 2 loaf tins. Oven temperature: 180 °C (350 °F, gas 4).

Carrot Cake

Makes 20 slices

---

250 g (8 oz, 2 cups)
  wholemeal self-raising
  flour
2.5 ml (½ tsp)
  bicarbonate of soda
10 ml (2 tsp) ground
  cinnamon
5 ml (1 tsp) grated
  nutmeg
5 ml (1 tsp) mixed spice
250 g (8 oz, 2 cups)
  grated carrot
30 g (1 oz, ½ cup)
  shredded coconut
60 g (2 oz, ½ cup)
  chopped walnuts
90 g (3 oz, ½ cup)
  sultanas
2 eggs
60 ml (4 tbsp, ½ cup)
  apple concentrate
250 ml (8 fl oz, 1 cup)
  skimmed or low-fat
  milk

Method:

1. Grease and lightly flour cake tin.
2. Sift flour, soda and spices. Return bran left in sieve to flour mixture.
3. Add carrot, coconut, nuts and sultanas.
4. Beat eggs until fluffy and add apple concentrate. Beat again and add milk.
5. Fold into dry ingredients. Stir until well mixed and pour batter into prepared cake tin.
6. Bake in a preheated oven until cooked through (about 40 – 45 minutes).
7. Turn out and cool on a wire rack.

To vary: replace walnuts with pecans

To store: keep in an airtight container for up to four days.

Nutritional data per slice: 475 kJ (113 cal), CHO 16 g, Protein 4 g, Fat 4 g.

Preparation time: 1 hour. Cooking equipment: 20 cm (8 inch) cake tin. Oven temperature: 200 °C (400 °F, gas 6).

Scones

Makes 12

---

125 g (4 oz, 1 cup)
  wholemeal self-raising
  flour
125 g (4 oz, 1 cup) self-
  raising flour, less
  20 ml (4 tsp)
20 ml (4 tsp) gluten flour
2.5 ml (½ tsp) baking
  powder
15 g (½ oz) margarine

Gluten flour is available from health food shops and some supermarkets. For perfect scones, handle the dough quickly and lightly so that it retains plenty of air and bake them in a hot oven.

Method:

1. In a bowl, combine the flours and baking powder. Use your fingertips to rub the margarine into the dry ingredients until the mixture resembles fine breadcrumbs.
2. Add the milk and yoghurt. Use a knife to work the mixture until you have a fine soft dough.

125 ml (4 fl oz, ½ cup)
low-fat milk
125 ml (4 fl oz, ½ cup)
low-fat plain yoghurt

_____

3. Turn the dough on to a lightly floured board. Using your finger-tips quickly and lightly knead the dough until soft and smooth.
4. Gently flatten the dough to a 2 cm (3/4 inch) thickness.
5. Use a scone cutter or sharp knife to shape twelve scones. Avoid re-rolling and cutting dough scraps more than once.
6. Place the scones on a lightly greased baking sheet. Leave a gap about half the width of a scone between each one.
7. If you want the scones to brown on top, brush each one with a little milk and bake them near the top of the oven.
8. Bake in a preheated oven for 8 – 10 minutes.

Nutritional data per scone: 454 kJ (108 cal), CHO 17 g, Protein 4 g, Fat 2 g.

Preparation time: 20 minutes. Cooking equipment: baking sheet. Oven temperature: 220 °C (425 °F, gas 7).

_____

Fruit Scones

Knead 45 g (1½ oz) sultanas, currants or chopped dates into the dough mixture at Step 2.

Bluestone Muffins

Makes 12

_____

150 g (5 oz, 1 cup) ripe
blueberries
20 ml (4 tsp) soft brown
sugar
250 g (8 oz, 2 cups)
wholemeal self-raising
flour
5 ml (1 tsp) baking
powder
5 ml (1 tsp) ground
cinnamon
1 egg
125 ml (4 fl oz, ½ cup)
low-fat berry yoghurt
250 ml (8 fl oz, 1 cup)
skimmed or low-fat
milk

_____

They look a little strange, perhaps, but taste terrific. Eat them fresh; they won't keep. Remember, a trace of sugar will not harm you, particularly when combined with plenty of complex carbohydrate and fibre.

Method:
1. Lightly grease muffin tins or spray with cooking spray.
2. Wash blueberries and combine with sugar in saucepan.
3. Heat gently until juice just starts to run.
4. Sift flour, baking powder and cinnamon into bowl. Return bran left in sieve to flour mixture.
5. Mix egg, yoghurt and milk in a bowl. Add to flour and blend until smooth.
6. Gently fold blueberries into mixture.
7. Spoon mixture into muffin tins, and bake in a preheated oven for 15 – 20 minutes until firm and very lightly browned.

Nutritional data per muffin: 486 kJ (116 cal), CHO 21 g, Protein 5 g, Fat 1 g.

Preparation time: 40 minutes. Cooking equipment: saucepan, muffin tins. Oven temperature: 220 °C (425 °F, gas 7).

Fruit (Christmas) Cake

Makes 24 slices

---

275 g (9 oz, 1½ cups)
   sultanas
90 g (3 oz, ½ cup) raisins,
   chopped
40 ml (8 tsp) brandy
20 ml (4 tsp) water
250 g (8 oz, 1 cup) sieved
   pumpkin (no lumps)
2 eggs, beaten
125 ml (4 fl oz, ½ cup)
   apple concentrate
125 ml (4 fl oz, ½ cup)
   skimmed or low-fat milk
60 g (2 oz, ½ cup)
   chopped pecans
5 ml (1 tsp) ground
   cinnamon
5 ml (1 tsp) mixed spice
125 g (4 oz, 1 cup) white
   self-raising flour
125 g (4 oz, 1 cup)
   wholemeal self-raising
   flour
2.5 ml (½ tsp)
   bicarbonate of soda

Apple concentrate gives sweetness to this wonderful fruity cake, and the dried fruit and pumpkin add plenty of fibre.

Method:
1. Mix sultanas, raisins, brandy and water; soak overnight.
2. Mix pumpkin, eggs, apple concentrate and milk.
3. Add soaked fruit, nuts and spices, then sifted flour and bicarbonate of soda. Return bran left in sieve to flour mixture. Mix well with a wooden spoon.
4. Spoon into a lightly greased cake tin.
5. Bake in a preheated oven for 10 minutes at 200 °C (400 °F, gas 6), then turn down the heat and bake at 180 °C (350 °F, gas 4) until cooked through and browned (about 1 – 11/4 hours). Cool on a wire rack.

To store: Keep in an airtight container for up to 1 week.

Nutritional data per slice: 482 kJ (115 cal), CHO 21 g, Protein 3 g. Fat 2 g.

Preparation time: 1½ hours, plus overnight soaking. Cooking equipment: round or square cake tin 20 cm (8 inches). Oven temperature: 200 °C (400 °F, gas 6), then 180 °C (350 °F, gas 4).

Mince Tarts

Makes 12

Filling:
60 g (2 oz, ½ cup) dried
   apricots, chopped
170 g (6 oz, 1 cup)
   sultanas
60 g (2 oz, ½ cup)
   chopped pitted dates
12 prunes, pitted and
   chopped

You can store any extra filling in a closed jar in the refrigerator for up to two weeks.

Method:
Filling:
1. Combine all ingredients in a saucepan.
2. Cook, covered, over low heat until apple is soft. Stir frequently to prevent sticking.
3. Spoon into bowl, cover and refrigerate overnight to blend flavours.

6 dried figs, chopped

60 g (2 oz, ½ cup) slivered
    almonds

2 apples, peeled, cored
    and thinly sliced

juice of ½ lemon

125 ml (4 fl oz, ½ cup)
    brandy

2.5 ml (½ tsp) ground
    cinnamon

2.5 ml (½ tsp) grated
    nutmeg

2.5 ml (½ tsp) mixed
    spice.

Pastry:

60 g (2 oz, ½ cup)
    wholemeal flour

125 g (4 oz, 1 cup) plain
    flour

90 g (3 oz) margarine

45 ml (9 tsp) iced water

1 egg yolk

few drops of liquid
    artificial sweetener

Pastry:

4. Sift flours into bowl, return bran left in sieve to sifted flour.

5. Rub margarine into flour until mixture resembles
   breadcrumbs.

6. In a cup, combine water, egg yolk and sweetener.

7. Add to flour mixture and stir in with a knife. Turn out on to
   floured board. Knead lightly, then cover and leave to rest for
   10 – 15 minutes.

8. Roll out dough and cut twelve rounds to fit the bottom of the
   tartlet tins. Cut another twelve, slightly smaller, to make lids.

9. Lightly grease the tartlet tins and line the bases.

10. Spoon some fruit mince into each.

11. Wet pastry edges and place remaining pastry rounds on top.
    Pinch edges to seal. Prick tops with fork.

12. Bake in a preheated oven for 20 – 30 minutes until lightly
    browned.

***Nutritional data per tart: 1130 kJ (270 cal), CHO 43 g,
Protein 5 g, Fat 9 g.***

*Preparation time: 1½ hours, plus overnight soaking. Cooking
equipment: saucepan, tartlet tins. Oven temperature: 190 °C
(375 °F, gas 5).*

Apple and Apricot Slice

Makes 16 pieces

1 quantity Wholemeal
    Pastry (page 186)

500 g (1 lb) fresh
    apricots, stoned and
    quartered, or 410 g
    (14 oz) canned apricot
    pieces

3 apples, peeled, cored
    and thinly sliced

2.5 ml (½ tsp) ground
    cinnamon

skimmed milk for glazing

Method:

1. Divide pastry into two equal pieces. Roll out first half and cover
   base of lightly greased baking tray.

2. Mix fruit and cinnamon and spread evenly on pastry.

3. Roll second half of pastry and place over fruit.

4. Prick surface of pastry with fork or skewer, brush with milk
   and bake in a preheated oven for 30 minutes or until pastry is
   beginning to brown.

5. Stand on wire rack for 5 minutes, loosen around the edges and
   turn out. Cool and cut into sixteen even slices.

***Nutritional data per serve: 569 kJ (136 cal), CHO 17 g,
Protein 3 g, Fat 7 g.***

*Preparation time: 50 minutes. Cooking equipment: baking sheets,
28 x 20 cm (11 x 8 inches). Oven temperature: 200 °C (400 °F, gas 6).*

Banana Muffins

Makes 12

2 very ripe bananas

1 egg

125 ml (4 fl oz, ½ cup)
skimmed or low-fat
milk

125 ml (4 fl oz, ½ cup)
unsweetened apple
juice

125 g (4 oz, 1 cup) wholemeal self-raising flour

125 g (4 oz, 1 cup) white
self-raising flour

2.5 ml (½ tsp) ground
cinnamon

2.5 ml (½ tsp) baking
powder

Method:

1. Mash bananas thoroughly; there should be no lumps.
2. Beat egg and add to banana.
3. Add milk and apple juice.
4. Sift flours, cinnamon and baking powder.
5. Fold flours into liquid mixture. Mix well by hand.
6. Spoon into very lightly greased muffin tins, filling each by about two-thirds.
7. Bake in a preheated oven for about 20 minutes until lightly browned and cooked through. Remove from oven, lift muffins out of tins and cool on a wire rack.

Nutritional data per muffin: 468 kJ (112 cal), CHO 21 g, Protein 4 g, Fat 1 g.

Preparation time: 40 minutes. Cooking equipment: muffin tins. Oven temperature: 220 °C (425 °F, gas 7).

Chris's Cookies

Makes 24 cookies

90 g (3 oz, 1 cup) rolled
oats

250 ml (8 oz, 1 cup)
wholemeal self-raising
flour

30 g (1 oz, ½ cup) rice
bran or oat bran

30 g (1 oz, ½ cup)
desiccated coconut

75 g (2½ oz, ½ cup)
currants

2 very ripe bananas,
mashed

2 eggs, beaten

You can use sultanas or chopped dried apricots instead of currants to make these quick and easy cookies.

Method:

1. Mix dry ingredients, add banana and eggs and mix well.
2. Break off small pieces, roll into balls, and place on lightly greased baking sheets. Flatten each ball with the back of a fork.
3. Bake in a preheated oven for about 15 minutes or until just beginning to brown.
4. Remove from baking sheets and cool on wire rack.

Nutritional data per cookie: 489 kJ (117 cal), CHO 18 g, Protein 4 g, Fat 3 g.

Preparation time: 25 minutes. Cooking equipment: 2 baking sheets. Oven temperature: 180 °C (350 °F, gas 4).

Date and Walnut Loaf

Makes 10 slices

125 ml (4 fl oz, ½ cup)
  boiling water
150 g (5 oz, 1 cup)
  chopped dates
185 g (6½ oz, 1½ cups)
  wholemeal self-raising
  flour
5 ml (1 tsp) mixed spice
5 ml (1 tsp) ground
  cinnamon
30 g (1 oz) margarine
20 ml (4 tsp) sugar
60 g (2 oz, ½ cup)
  chopped walnuts
1 egg, beaten
250 ml (8 fl oz, 1 cup)
  skimmed milk

Method:

1. Pour boiling water over dates and leave to stand for 30 minutes.
2. Mix flour and spices in bowl.
3. Rub in margarine until mixture resembles breadcrumbs.
4. Add sugar, dates, soaking water and walnuts to dry mixture and mix lightly.
5. Stir in egg and skimmed milk.
6. Place in lightly greased loaf tin.
7. Bake upright in a preheated oven for 45 minutes or until cooked.
8. Leave in tin for 10 minutes before turning out to cool.

Nutritional data per slice: 976 kJ (233 cal), CHO 35 g, Protein 6 g, Fat 8 g.

Preparation time: 1 hour and 10 minutes. Cooking equipment: loaf tin. Oven temperature: 190 °C (375 °F, gas 5), then 180 °C (350 °F, gas 4) if longer time needed.

After-Dinner Treats

Date Rolls

Makes 20 pieces

300 g (10 oz, 2 cups)
  pitted dates
juice of 1 lemon
2.5 ml (½ tsp) ground
  cinnamon
60 g (2 oz, ½ cup)
  crushed, roasted
  hazelnuts
15 g (1 oz) poppy seeds
4 wheatmeal biscuits,
  crushed

Method:

1. Blend dates with lemon juice and cinnamon to a thick paste.
2. Add nuts and poppy seeds and mix well.
3. Form into four rolls, each about 10 cm (4 inches) long and 2.5 cm (1 inch) thick. Roll in crushed wheatmeal biscuits.
4. Refrigerate for 2 hours, and then cut each roll into five equal pieces, about 2 cm (3/4 inch) thick.

Nutritional data per piece: 313 kJ (75 cal), CHO 13 g, Protein 2 g, Fat 2 g.

Preparation time: 30 minutes. Cooking equipment: food processor or blender.

Rum Balls

Makes 24

20 wheatmeal biscuits,
  crushed
40 ml (8 tsp) cocoa
  powder
150 g (5 oz) ricotta cheese
60 ml (2 fl oz, ¼ cup)
  unsweetened apple
  juice
40 ml (8 tsp) dark rum
few drops of vanilla
  essence (optional)
45 g (1 ½ oz, 1 cup)
  desiccated coconut

Method:

1. Process biscuits in food processor or blend until they resemble fine crumbs.
2. Add cocoa, ricotta cheese, apple juice, rum and vanilla and blend well.
3. Spoon into a mixing bowl, cover and refrigerate overnight.
4. Roll a small spoonful of mixture in coconut, place on tray and refrigerate.

To vary: add 45 g (1½ oz, ¼ cup) chopped raisins.

To store: keep in airtight container for up to a week.

Nutritional data per ball: 327 kJ (78 cal), CHO 8 g, Protein 2 g, Fat 4 g.

Preparation time: 30 minutes, spread over two days, plus overnight. Cooking equipment: food processor or blender.

Frozen Fruit

Serves 4

8 strawberries, tops left
  on
20 red grapes, preferably
  small
½ slice fresh, ripe
  pineapple
2 kiwi fruit
garnish: mint or
  strawberry leaves

We have used fresh strawberries, grapes, pineapple and kiwi fruit in this recipe but you can use any selection of fresh fruit in season. You can also use frozen fruit to garnish drinks.

Method:

1. Wash and dry strawberries and grapes.
2. Cut pineapple into eight chunks.
3. Peel kiwi fruit and cut into four pieces.
4. Place fruit on dish and freeze for about 2 hours until firm.
5. Transfer frozen fruit to glass serving plate and allow to thaw for 10 – 15 minutes. Decorate with leaves.

To store: sealed, in freezer, if it is to be kept for more than 24 hours.

Nutritional data per serve: 123 kJ (30 cal), CHO 7 g, Protein 1 g, Fat 0 g.

Preparation time: 2 ½ hours. Cooking equipment: tray or shallow dish.

Fruit Cheese

***Makes 1 log about
20 cm (8 inches) long***

90 g (3 oz, ½ cup) dried
   mixed fruit
125 ml (4 fl oz, ½ cup)
   hot water
60 ml (2 fl oz, ¼ cup)
   brandy
125 g (4 oz) each of
   cottage cheese and
   cream cheese or 250 g
   (8 oz) low-fat cream
   cheese
15 g (1/2 oz) poppy seeds

This after-dinner treat can be made one or two days before serving
and then be stored in the refrigerator until needed.

Method:

1. Place fruit in bowl and pour over water and brandy. Allow to
   soak for about 12 hours until fruit is swollen and soft.
2. Drain fruit, retaining the liquid.
3. Blend cheese and about 45 ml ($1\frac{1}{2}$ fl oz) of the drained liquid
   until smooth. Discard remaining drained liquid.
4. Stir fruit into mixture and mix well.
5. Tip mixture on to clingfilm (plastic wrap). Form into a rough
   log shape. Roll clingfilm (plastic wrap) around log and
   refrigerate for 1 hour to set.
6. Spread poppy seeds over a clean piece of clingfilm (plastic
   wrap) and roll cheese log on this to coat with seeds. Return to
   refrigerator for 2 hours before serving.

To store: cover and refrigerate for up to four days.

Nutritional data per total quantity: 4221 kJ (1008 cal), CHO 72 g, Protein 45 g, Fat 47 g.

Preparation time: 10 minutes, plus 12 hours soaking time and 3 hours setting time.

Drinks

Note: Alcohol provides 29 kJ (7 cal) per gram.

50/50 Swirl
Serves 4

For special occasions, use chilled champagne instead of bitter lemon.

Pour 450 ml (3/4 pint, 2 cups) unsweetened orange juice into a shallow tray and freeze until almost set. Crush and spoon into four chilled glasses. Pour 300 ml (1/2 pint, 11/2 cups) low-calorie (low-joule) bitter lemon into each glass and add a swirl of lemon and orange peel.

Nutritional data per serve: 175 kJ (42 cal), CHO 9 g, Protein 1 g, Fat 0 g.

Orange Buttermilk
Serves 4

Place 375 ml (12 fl oz, 11/2 cups) buttermilk in a jug, then slowly add 375 ml (12 fl oz, 11/2 cups) unsweetened orange juice, stirring constantly. Sweeten with artificial sweetener if desired, pour into glasses and add ice-cubes.

Nutritional data per serve: 262 kJ (63 cal), CHO 11 g, Protein 4 g, Fat 0 g.

Strawberry Granita
Serves 2

Wash and hull 250 g (8 oz) strawberries and add to food processor or blender with 8 – 10 ice-cubes and the juice of an orange. Blend until ice is crushed. Add artifical sweetener to taste, then quickly blend again. Pour into glasses.

Nutritional data per serve: 164 kJ (39 cal), CHO 7 g, Protein 2 g, Fat 0 g.

Irish Coffee
Serves 4

Bring 125 ml (4 fl oz, 1/2 cup) whisky to the boil and simmer for 30 seconds (or microwave on High for 1 minute). Pour into four cups, top with hot black coffee and a tablespoon of Creamy Whipped Topping (page 163). Sweeten to taste with artificial sweetener.

Nutritional data per serve: 371 kJ (90 cal), CHO 2 g, Protein 1 g, Fat 0 g.

Apricot Cooler
Serves 4

Place 410 g (14 oz) canned unsweetened apricot pieces and 125 ml (4 fl oz, 1/2 cup) unsweetened apricot nectar or orange juice in a food processor or blender. Blend until smooth. Chill well, then pour into four glasses. Top with soda water and garnish with mint.

Nutritional data per serve: 183 kJ (44 cal), CHO 11 g, Protein 1 g, Fat 0 g.

Sangria

Serves 4

Bring 450 ml (3/4 pint, 2 cups) claret and 125 ml (4 fl oz, 1/2 cup) water to the boil in a saucepan and simmer for 30 seconds. Thinly slice one orange and one lemon and place in a jug. Pour wine over the lemon and orange slices and marinate in the refrigerator for 4 hours. Strain the mixture, add 125 ml (4 fl oz, 1/2 cup) unsweetened orange juice, sweeten to taste with artificial sweetener and serve with two ice-cubes and an orange slice.

Nutritional data per serve: 375 kJ (91 cal), CHO 2 g, Protein 0 g, Fat 0 g.

Hot Claret Punch

Serves 4

Combine 600 ml (1 pint, 2 1/2 cups) claret and 60 ml (2 fl oz, 1/4 cup) brandy in a saucepan or microwave dish. Bring to the boil and simmer for 30 seconds, or microwave on High for 4 minutes. Sweeten to taste with artificial sweetener, pour into glasses and sprinkle with grated nutmeg.

Nutritional data per serve: 433 kJ (105 cal), CHO 1 g, Protein 0 g, Fat 0 g.

Cherries and Leben

Serves 2

Place 75 g (2 1/2 oz, 1/2 cup) fresh cherries in a food processor or blender and blend until smooth. Add 175 ml (6 fl oz, 3/4 cup) low-fat milk and 175 ml (6 fl oz, 3/4 cup) low-fat plain yoghurt, good pinch of ground cinnamon, artificial sweetener equivalent to 10 ml (2 tsp) sugar, and 4 – 6 ice-cubes. Blend again until thoroughly combined. Pour into glasses and serve.

Nutritional data per serve: 551 kJ (132 cal), CHO 17 g, Protein 10 g, Fat 3 g.

Kiwi Cooler

Serves 4

Peel four kiwi fruit and place in food processor or blender with two peeled and stoned peaches, two peeled and chopped bananas, 450 ml (3/4 pint, 2 cups) unsweetened pineapple juice and 8 – 10 ice-cubes. Blend until ice is crushed. Pour into four glasses and garnish with a sprig of mint.

Nutritional data per serve: 539 kJ (129 cal), CHO 30 g, Protein 2 g, Fat 0 g.

Hot Milk Sleeper

Serves 1

Separate an egg, beat the white until stiff and beat the yolk separately with 30 ml (1 fl oz) brandy and a few drops of vanilla essence. Heat 200 ml (7 fl oz) skimmed or low-fat milk and add to egg yolk mixture. Fold in egg white and sweeten to taste with artificial sweetener. Pour into a large mug, sprinkle with grated nutmeg and serve.

Nutritional data per serve: 1174 kJ (285 cal), CHO 10 g, Protein 13 g, Fat 5 g.

CALCULATING YOUR NEEDS AND DESIGNING MEAL PLANS

This section shows you how your individual needs are assessed and how this information is used by your diabetic team to make an effective, balanced eating plan for you. This will enable you to become confident about your own ability to eat well and control your diabetes.

Assessing your personal needs

Several points must be considered so your diabetic team can determine what your kilojoule (calorie) needs are:
- Do you have to lose weight or gain weight? This will make a significant difference to the calculations.
- How tall are you? Height is an important factor in working out what your weight should be.
- What is your activity level? Again, how hard you work physically and your level of exercise will have an important impact on your kilojoule (calorie) needs. The more active you are, the more energy you need. You should therefore discuss your lifestyle with your diabetic team.

Working out how much carbohydrate, protein and fat you need

When you know what your total kilojoules (calories) ought to be, depending on your weight, height and activity levels, you need to know the proportions of carbohydrate, protein and fat you require. You may find that this is quite different from what you have been eating because, average diet tends to include too much fat and protein and not enough carbohydrate.

Carbohydrate should provide **50 – 60 per cent** of your daily intake of energy. The average intake of energy from **protein** should be **15 – 20 per cent**, while the **fat** average should be **30 – 35 per cent**.

To ensure an adequate protein intake where energy levels are low, the percentage contribution from protein may need to be increased and the percentage from fat and carbohydrate decreased slightly (see example meal plans pages 32 – 37).

What about alcohol? Alcohol contains kilojoules (calories): we have given a ready-reckoner for alcoholic drinks on page 202.

If you don't have to lose weight, you may include up to two standard drinks a day, always taken with carbohydrate, but if you need to plan your diet accurately, you must deduct their value in kilojoules (calories) from your daily total. In other words if you include alcoholic drinks, you must cut down on your other food — preferably, by eating a little less of everything.

If you are overweight, we suggest you drink alcohol only on special occasions, and then limit your intake to two standard drinks.

Considering your diabetes

Are you on medication or not?

If you are not on medication, then in most cases, spreading your carbohydrate intake evenly between three meals a day is best, although it is not essential. Avoid eating snacks between meals if you are overweight.

If you are on medication, then you need to ask your diabetic team what type and when to take it. Find out about your medication so that your eating plan allows your carbohydrate to be spread in such a way as to keep your blood glucose level within normal range.

When taking insulin, it is important to ensure an adequate carbohydrate intake at times when the insulin is most active. An even spread of carbohydrate between three meals daily is usually best, although some people find it easier to regulate blood glucose levels if they eat a carbohydrate-rich snack between meals. Sometimes you may need to alter the distribution of carbohydrate to match more closely insulin activity and help to prevent hyper- or hypoglycaemia.

It is also important to **keep your carbohydrate intake even from day to day** to prevent unwanted swings in blood glucose level.

Remember, having diabetes does not affect your needs for energy, carbohydrate, protein and fat. It only affects the timing and planning of your meals. On the other hand, your meals and meal pattern must suit your lifestyle and it may be easier to change the timing and dose of your medication rather than your established eating pattern. This must be discussed thoroughly with your diabetic team.

Converting the information into daily meal plans

The sample meal plans on pages 32 – 37 show you how to use this information to achieve a well-balanced diet.

THE DETAILED FOOD VALUE LIST

This food value chart will help you to find out more about different types of food. It is not an essential part of your diabetes management, but you may find it interesting and useful. Most people use only a limited range of food in their day-to-day eating pattern. This list may encourage you to experiment and include a wider variety of food, both when eating at home or when having a meal in a restaurant or in friends' homes.

We have given the quantity of foods as 'average serves' to give you a measuring stick for the amount of energy, carbohydrate, protein and fat in different food items. It will allow you to compare foods, and immediately identify those foods high or low in carbohydrate, protein or fat.

Foods vary greatly in their nutrition content, depending on such things as place of origin, ripeness and season. In view of this, we have rounded off all figures to the nearest whole number. So use the chart as a guide only to nutrition values. The density factor of different foods varies considerably so a standard 250 ml (8 fl oz) measuring cup has been used to calculate serves in the following list. Brand names may vary in the United Kingdom, Australia, New Zealand and South Africa.

Food Measure	Serve	g	Energy kJ	Energy Cal	C g	P g	F g

Breads

Food Measure	Serve	g	kJ	Cal	C g	P g	F g
Bagel	1 med	80	720	179	32	8	3
Bread roll, white	1 small	60	649	155	29	6	2
Bread roll, wholemeal	1 small	60	600	143	26	6	1
Breadcrumbs, dried	40 ml	20	302	72	14	2	1
Crumpet	1 med	40	314	75	16	2	neg
Fibre increased	1 slice	30	270	67	12	3	1
Flatbread/pitta	1 large	100	1122	268	52	9	2
	1 small	60	673	161	31	5	1
Matzos	1	23	288	69	14	2	1
Muffin	1 whole	70	640	153	29	6	1
Raisin	1 slice	30	329	79	16	2	1
Rye/black	1 slice	50	424	101	19	4	1
White	1 slice	30	291	70	13	2	1
Wholemeal/multigrain	1 slice	30	271	65	12	3	1

Biscuits

Food Measure	Serve	g	kJ	Cal	C g	P g	F g
Crackerbread ™	4	28	482	115	19	4	3
Gingernuts	2	27	470	112	23	1	2
Krispy wheat ™/ Sesawheat ™	4	20	384	92	14	2	3
Marie	2	16	300	70	13	1	2
Morning Coffee ™	2	16	290	68	13	1	2
Rye Cruskits ™	4	20	306	73	15	3	1
Ryvita ™	2	20	301	72	16	2	1
Salada, plain ™	4 small	16	260	64	11	2	2
Salada, wholemeal ™	4 small	14	240	56	10	2	1
Sao ™	2	18	329	79	12	2	3
Savoy ™	6	25	470	113	17	2	5
Shredded Wheat ™	2	16	270	64	11	1	2
Thin Captains ™	4	22	380	92	17	3	2
Uneeda ™	4	22	400	94	16	2	3
Vitawheat ™	4	28	480	112	20	2	3

Breakfast Cereals

Food Measure	Serve	g	kJ	Cal	C g	P g	F g
All bran	1/2 cup	20	231	55	8	3	1
Bran Flakes ™	1 cup	45	618	148	28	6	1
Cornflakes ™	1 cup	30	465	111	26	3	neg
Muesli, unsweetened, untoasted	1/2 cup	55	846	202	31	7	5
Oat bran, raw	20 ml	11	113	27	7	2	1
Puffed Wheat ™	1 cup	12	182	43	9	2	neg
Rice Bubbles ™	1 cup	30	444	106	25	2	neg
Rolled oats, cooked	1 cup	260	551	132	22	4	3
Rolled oats, raw	1/3 cup	35	568	136	25	5	3
Wheat flake biscuits, e.g. Weetabix ™, Vitabrits ™	2	30	398	95	19	3	neg
Wheat flakes, e.g. Weeties ™	1 cup	30	452	108	22	4	neg
Wheat germ	40 ml	10	128	30	4	3	1

Flour and other Cereals

Food Measure	Serve	g	kJ	Cal	C g	P g	F g
Buckwheat groats, raw	1/2 cup	50	760	182	42	4	0
Cornflour	40 ml	20	312	75	20	neg	0
Cracker wheat/kibbled wheat/bulgar/ burghul/ pearled wheat, dry	1/4 cup	45	563	134	27	5	1
Custard powder	40 ml	20	292	70	17	neg	0
Egg pasta, cooked	1 cup	200	1093	261	51	10	1
Flour, white	40 ml	20	295	70	15	2	neg
Flour, wholemeal	40 ml	20	235	56	10	2	neg
Pasta, macaroni, spaghetti, cooked	1 cup	140	699	167	34	6	neg
Pasta, macaroni, spaghetti, raw		100	1426	341	70	11	1
Pearl barley	40 ml	35	446	107	21	3	1
Rice, brown, cooked	1 cup	180	1134	271	57	6	2
Rice, brown, raw	60 ml	60	919	220	46	5	1
Rice, white, cooked	1 cup	190	993	237	53	4	neg
Rice, white, raw	60 ml	60	885	211	48	4	neg
Sago, dry	40 ml	20	300	72	18	neg	0
Semolina, dry	40 ml	20	300	72	16	2	neg

Pulses

Food Measure	Serve	g	kJ	Cal	C g	P g	F g
Baked beans, canned with tomato sauce	1/2 cup	120	324	77	12	6	1
Chick-peas, cooked	1 cup	160	848	203	28	13	neg
uncooked	20 ml	25	339	81	11	5	neg
Dried beans (borlotti, white, black-eyed etc. cooked	1/2 cup	90	375	84	17	6	neg
uncooked	20 ml	25	290	69	10	6	neg
Lentils, cooked	1/2 cup	70	294	69	13	6	neg
uncooked	20 ml	25	352	84	15	6	neg
Mixed bean salad, canned	1/2 cup	100	446	106	17	6	1
Soya bean curd (tofu)	1/2 cup	110	303	72	2	8	6
Soya beans, canned	1/2 cup	100	466	111	11	10	4
raw	20 ml	25	426	102	9	9	4
Split peas, cooked	1/2 cup	90	433	103	19	7	neg
raw	20 ml	25	364	87	16	6	neg

Starchy vegetables cooked edible portion

Food Measure	Serve	g	kJ	Cal	C g	P g	F g
Beetroot	1/2 cup	100	173	41	8	2	0
Parsnip	1/2 cup	75	156	38	8	1	1
Potatoes	1 med	120	330	70	16	3	0
Pumpkin	1/2 cup	85	175	42	8	2	0
Sweetcorn	1/2 cup	85	470	112	22	2	2
Sweet potato	1/2 cup	120	377	92	21	2	0
Yams	1/2 cup	120	473	113	27	3	0

* C = Carbohydrate   P = Protein   F = Fat   A = Alcohol   neg = negligible

Food Measure	Serve	g	Energy kJ	Cal	C g	P g	F g

Other vegetables

Where ½ cup of cooked vegetables provides 5 g or less of carbohydrate, we have classified them as 'low starch vegetables'. These vegetables are also low in kilojoules (calories), protein and fat, but high in vitamins, minerals and fibre. Include some in your meal plan every day.

Artichoke, globe	Kale
Asparagus	Kohlrabi
Aubergine (eggplant, brinjal)	Lettuce
Bean shoots/sprouts	Marrow
Beans, French	Mushrooms
Broad beans	Mung beans/sprouts
Broccoli	Onions
Brussels sprouts	Parsley
Cabbage	Peas
Capsicum (bell pepper)	Pepper (capsicum)
Carrots	Radish
Cauliflower	Spinach
Celery	Summer squash
Chinese cabbage	Swedes
Chokoes	Swiss chard
Courgettes (zucchini, baby marrows)	(silverbeet)
Cucumbers	Tomatoes
Endive	Turnips
Garlic	Watercress

Fruit, edible portion

Food Measure	Serve	g	kJ	Cal	C g	P g	F g
Apple, canned/stewed	1 cup	240	237	79	20	0	0
Apple, fresh	1 med	120	235	56	14	0	0
Apple juice	1/2 cup	120	170	41	10	0	0
Apricot canned/stewed	1 cup	230	228	55	12	2	0
Apricot, dried	10 hlvs	40	310	74	17	2	0
Apricot, fresh	3 med	90	105	25	6	1	0
Avocado	1/4 med	75	659	157	0	1	17
Banana	1 med	100	384	92	21	2	0
Berries, blackberry, raspberry	1 cup	133	140	33	7	1	0
Berries, blueberry	1 cup	133	320	76	19	1	0
Berries, strawberry	12 med	100	81	19	3	2	0
Cantaloup (rock melon), small	half	200	182	43	10	2	0
Cherries	20 med	100	201	48	12	1	0
Custard apple	1/2 med	75	230	55	12	1	0
Date, dried	5 whole	40	422	101	25	1	0
Fig, dried	2 whole	30	272	65	16	1	0
Fig, fresh	2 whole	95	161	30	8	1	0
Gooseberry, stewed, unsweetened	1/2 cup	125	78	19	4	1	0
Grapefruit, fresh	half	120	133	32	6	1	0
Grapefruit juice, unsweetened	1/2 cup	120	152	36	8	0	0
Grapes	20	100	256	61	15	1	0
Honeydew melon	1/4 med	150	194	46	10	1	0
Kiwi fruit	1 med	60	124	29	6	1	0

Fruit, edible portion (cont.)

Food Measure	Serve	g	kJ	Cal	C g	P g	F g
Lemon	1 med	50	48	12	2	0	0
Lime	1 med	30	27	6	0	0	0
Lychee	8 whole	100	286	68	16	1	0
Mandarin	1 med	75	122	29	6	1	0
Mango	1 med	120	283	67	16	1	0
Nectarine	2 med	100	156	37	8	1	0
Orange	1 med	150	234	56	12	2	0
Orange juice, commercial unsweetened	1/2 cup	120	175	42	9	1	0
Passion fruit, pulp	1 med	20	39	9	1	1	0
Pawpaw	1 cup	240	296	70	16	0	0
Peach, canned, unsweetened	1 cup	220	230	55	13	2	0
Peach, fresh	1	110	145	35	7	1	0
Pear, canned, unsweetened	1 cup	200	220	53	13	0	0
Pear, fresh	1	150	317	76	19	0	0
Pineapple, canned, unsweetened	2 slices	100	187	45	10	1	0
Pineapple, fresh	1 slice	140	221	53	11	2	0
Pineapple juice	1/2 cup	120	244	58	14	0	0
Plum	3	100	164	39	10	1	0
Prune, dried	6 med	50	343	82	20	1	0
Quince, stewed, unsweetened	1/2 cup	125	170	41	10	0	0
Raisin/sultana/currant	20 ml	13	136	33	8	0	0
Rhubarb, stewed, unsweetened	1/2 cup	130	33	8	1	1	0
Tamarillo, peeled	1 med	50	56	13	2	1	0
Watermelon	1 cup	220	211	50	11	1	0

* An average serve of many of the fruits in this list will contribute only a small amount of carbohydrate and kilojoules (calories). If the serve size (or part of a serve) contains 5 g or less of carbohydrate, there is no need to count it as part of your meal plan. However, if you eat several serves of low-carbohydrate fruits throughout the day they will contribute significantly to your carbohydrate and kilojoule (calorie) intake.

* C = Carbohydrate   P = Protein   F = Fat   A = Alcohol   neg = negligible

Food Measure	Serve	g	kJ	Cal	C g	P g	F g
Milk and dairy products							
Cheese							
Cheddar		30	504	120	0	8	10
cottage, low-fat	1/2 cup	100	362	86	2	18	1
cream		30	431	103	0	2	10
low-fat hard 7%		30	242	58	0	10	2
low-fat hard 18%		30	360	90	0	20	5
ricotta, low-fat		60	332	79	1	7	5
Ice-cream	40 ml	50	352	84	12	2	3
Milk							
2% fat	1 cup	260	606	145	15	10	5
evaporated, full-cream	1/2 cup	162	1069	255	18	14	15
evaporated, skimmed	1/2 cup	162	689	164	24	17	0
full-cream	1 cup	260	707	169	12	9	10
powder, full-cream	60 ml	27	554	132	11	7	7
powder, skimmed	60 ml	33	499	119	17	12	0
skimmed	1 cup	260	369	88	13	9	0
Yoghurt							
full-cream flavoured/ fruit	1 small	200	826	197	32	10	4
full-cream, plain	1 small	200	650	155	13	9	8
low-fat flavoured/ fruit	1 small	200	744	178	32	10	2
low-fat, plain	1 small	200	420	110	0	13	12
Meat and meat products							
Beef, lean, minced		120	581	139	0	26	4
Beef, raw, lean only		120	602	144	0	26	4
Ham, leg, lean	1 slice	30	136	32	0	6	1
Lamb, raw, lean only		120	608	145	0	26	4
Liver		120	816	195	3	26	9
Luncheon meat	1 slice	30	321	77	1	4	6
Pork, raw, lean only		120	531	127	0	27	2
Pork sausage, cooked	2 thin	75	990	237	8	10	18
Salami, thin slices	3	30	538	128	0	7	11
Veal, raw, lean only		120	531	127	0	27	2
Poultry							
Chicken, breast, no skin, raw		120	563	135	0	27	3
Fish and seafood							
Fish, raw fillet	med	100	386	92	0	18	2
Oysters, raw	6	60	130	31	0	6	1
Prawns, boiled		100	451	108	0	22	2
Tuna/salmon, canned in brine, drained	1/2 cup	90	411	98	0	20	2
Tuna, canned in oil, fish incl. oil	1/2 cup	90	1082	258	0	20	0

Food Measure	Serve	g	kJ	Cal	C g	P g	F g
Protein foods (cont.)							
Eggs							
Egg, hen (55 g)	1 med	47	288	69	0	6	5
Nuts							
Almonds, raw	1/3 cup	50	1168	278	2	5	27
Peanut butter	20 ml	20	516	123	2	5	11
Peanuts, raw	1/3	50	1182	281	5	12	25
Pecan, raw	1/3	50	1379	328	11	4	33
Pinenuts, raw	40 ml	20	498	119	3	4	11
Fats							
Cream, thickened	40 ml	40	547	131	1	1	14
Dressing, French, commercial	40 ml	40	625	149	3	0	16
Margarine, butter	20 ml	20	608	145	0	0	16
Mayonnaise, light, commercial	20 ml	20	258	62	3	0	5
Oil, blended, polyunsaturated	20 ml		702	168	0	0	19
Olives, in brine	4 med	27	113	27	0	0	3
Popcorn, plain		20	353	84	14	3	2
Potato chips (fries)	10 chips	85	394	94	2	15	2
Potato crisps, plain small packet	1	25	526	126	12	2	8

Alcoholic beverages

One standard drink = about 10 g alcohol and 335 kilojoules (80 calories) with the exception of alcohol-reduced drinks:

	ml	kJ	Cal	C g	A g
Beer, 3.5 – 4% alcohol	200	335	80	6	7 – 8
Champagne, dry	100	350	65	neg-2	12
Cider	200	335	80	2	10
Diet ale, 3.5 – 4% alcohol	200	290	70	3	7-8
Extra light beer, 1% alc.	200	135-210	32-50	8-10	2
Light beer, 2 – 3% alcohol	200	190-250	46-60	4-6	4-6
Liqueurs	20	300	70	6	7
Port	60	260	60	8	10
Sherry, dry	60	335	80	1	9
Sherry, sweet	60	365	90	4	11
Spirits, brandy, gin, whisky, rum	30	276	66	0	10
Stout	200	335	80	4	9
Vermouth, dry	60	335	80	1	11
Vermouth, sweet	60	365	90	4	11
Wine, red, claret	100	350	85	neg	12
Wine, white, riesling	100	350	85	neg	12
Wine, white, Sauternes	100	370	90	4	11

* C = Carbohydrate   P = Protein   F = Fat   A = Alcohol   neg = negligible

INDEX